Volume 1 Grade 2

Common Core State Standards

Write-in Literacy Handbook

McGraw Hill Education

Bothell, WA • Chicago, IL • Columbus, OH • New York, NY

Image Credit: **Cover** Wetzel and Company

The McGraw-Hill Companies

Send all inquiries to:
McGraw-Hill Education
8787 Orion Place
Columbus, OH 43240

ISBN: 978-0-02-117078-4
MHID: 0-02-117078-9

Printed in the United States of America.

3 4 5 6 7 8 9 RHR 16 15 14 13 12

Contents

Grade 2

Part 1
READING: LITERATURE

Part 2
READING: INFORMATIONAL TEXT

Part 4
WRITING

4.1 Text Types and Purposes

4.2 Production and Distribution

4.3 Research to Build and Present Knowledge

Part 1
READING LITERATURE
1.1 Key Ideas and Details

Standard 1

1

Lesson A

Ask and Answer Questions

Good readers ask questions as they read. Sometimes the answers can be found in the story. Other times readers must use what they already know to answer the questions.

Follow these steps when reading:

1. **Start with a question word, such as *who, what, where, when, why,* or *how.***
2. **Think about how you can find the answer.**
3. **Answer your question.**

Now look at a model to see how to ask and answer questions as you read.

Ask and Answer Questions Model

Read the story below.

Don't Feed the Bears

Deanna was camping with her family. Sitting by the campfire, Deanna's dad talked about the bears that sometimes came through the woods. He told Deanna that the bears were wild and often hungry. After dinner Deanna's mother put all of their food away. She didn't want the bears to smell it.

Deanna was getting ready for bed. Then she found half of a sandwich in her backpack. She thought about the hungry bears. Maybe the sandwich would feed them. Deanna took the sandwich outside. Her father saw her just in time.

"No, Deanna!" her dad called out. "Never feed a wild bear!"

Now learn more about how to follow the three steps.

Ask Questions

What questions do you have about the story? Think about who, what, where, when, why, and how.

Here are some questions you might ask to help you understand the story better.

1. *Who* are the people camping?
2. *Why* did Deanna's mom put the food away?
3. *How* did Deanna's dad stop her from feeding a bear?

Now let's see how you will find the answers to your questions.

1

Find Answers

To find the answers to your questions, you can reread, or read again. Look for clues in the text that will help you answer your questions. The clues are underlined below.

1. *Who* are the people camping?

Don't Feed the Bears

Deanna was camping with her family. Sitting by the campfire, Deanna's dad talked about the bears that sometimes came through the woods. He told Deanna that the bears were wild and often hungry. After dinner Deanna's mother put all of their food away. She didn't want the bears to smell it.

Deanna was getting ready for bed. Then she found half of a sandwich in her backpack. She thought about the hungry bears. Maybe the sandwich would feed them. Deanna took the sandwich outside. Her father saw her just in time.

"No, Deanna!" her dad called out. "Never feed a wild bear!"

2. *Why* did Deanna's mom put the food away?

Don't Feed the Bears

Deanna was camping with her family. Sitting by the campfire, Deanna's dad talked about the bears that sometimes came through the woods. He told Deanna that the bears were wild and often hungry. After dinner Deanna's mother put all of their food away. She didn't want the bears to smell it.

Deanna was getting ready for bed. Then she found half of a sandwich in her backpack. She thought about the hungry bears. Maybe the sandwich would feed them. Deanna took the sandwich outside. Her father saw her just in time.

"No, Deanna!" her dad called out. "Never feed a wild bear!"

1

3. *How* did Deanna's dad stop her from feeding a bear?

Don't Feed the Bears

Deanna was camping with her family. Sitting by the campfire, Deanna's dad talked about the bears that sometimes came through the woods. He told Deanna that the bears were wild and often hungry. After dinner Deanna's mother put all of their food away. She didn't want the bears to smell it.

Deanna was getting ready for bed. Then she found half of a sandwich in her backpack. She thought about the hungry bears. Maybe the sandwich would feed them. Deanna took the sandwich outside. Her father saw her just in time.

"No, Deanna!" her dad called out. "Never feed a wild bear!"

Answers

Now that you have read the passage, you can answer the questions.

1. **Question:** *Who* are the people camping?
   Answer: Deanna is camping with her family, her mom and dad.
2. **Question:** *Why* did Deanna's mom put the food away?

   Answer: She didn't want the bears to smell it.
3. **Question:** *How* did Deanna's dad stop her from feeding a bear?

   Answer: He told her never to feed a wild bear.

You have asked questions about **key details**. Key details tell more about the main idea of a story.

Now turn to pages 8–9 to practice asking and answering questions.

Name ______________________

Ask and Answer Questions

Practice

Read the story.

Snip Shop

Luis went to see his father after school. When he got to his father's shop, he walked through the door. A bell went off. Luis's father looked over and smiled. Then he went back to work. His father was cutting a man's hair.

The man sat in a high chair and wore a black cape over his shirt. Luis's father snipped at the hair with scissors. Then he combed the hair. Finally, he dried it and put some spray on it. When he was finished, he gave the man a mirror. The man smiled. "Next," Luis's father said.

Read the story again to answer these questions:

Why did a bell go off?
What does Luis's father do for a job?

Name ______________________

Write your answers.

1. Why did a bell go off?

____

____

2. What does Luis's father do for a job?

____

____

3. What is another question you could ask about this story?

____

____

4. Answer the question you just wrote.

____

____

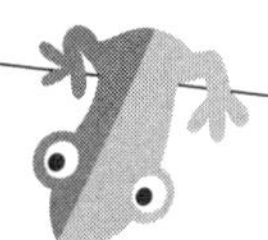

Lesson B

Recount Stories from Diverse Cultures

When you **recount** a story, you tell what happened at the beginning, middle, and end. You use your own words and tell only the important parts. Retelling the important parts, or **plot**, will help you understand the lesson or moral in a story.

In this lesson you will learn more about recounting two different kinds of stories: fables and folktales.

Fable

A fable is a short story that has a **moral**. A moral is a lesson. A fable often has animals or other objects that speak as if they were humans. Many fables have been told and retold for thousands of years.

Read the Greek fable.

The Wind and the Sun

One day the Wind and the Sun were having an argument. They couldn't agree about who was stronger.

"I'm strong," said the Wind to the Sun.

"So am I," said the Sun.

"Let's have a contest to find out who's stronger," said the Sun. "Can you see that man down there? He's wearing a heavy coat. Let's see who can make him take it off."

"I'll go first," said the Wind. The Wind started to blow. Brrr! The man shivered, but he didn't take off his coat.

The Wind blew harder. It was very cold. The man held onto his hat, and wrapped his scarf around his neck. He kept on walking, and he didn't take off his coat.

"Now it's my turn," said the Sun. The Sun started to shine. The man felt hot, but he didn't take off his coat. He took off his hat and then his scarf. But he kept his coat on.

The Sun shone more brightly. The man felt hotter than ever. At last he stopped walking. He took off his coat.

The Wind knew he was defeated, so he left in a bad mood.

"You are strong, but I'm stronger," called the Sun. "Gently leading is better than a lot of force."

When you **recount** a fable, you use your own words to tell the important parts of the story. One way to recount a fable's plot is to use a sequence chart. In a sequence chart you retell what happened in order from beginning to end.

Sequence Chart

This chart helps you organize the important parts of the fable. You can write the events in the order they happened. If you can't recount the order of events, you can reread the fable to help you.

SEQUENCE CHART
Sun and Wind decide to have a contest to see who is stronger. The contest is to get a man to take off his coat.
Wind tries to get the man to take off his coat by blowing really hard. The man still doesn't take off his coat.
Sun tries to get the man to take off his coat by shining brightly and getting warm.
Sun wins the argument. The man takes off his coat.

Moral

Fables teach a **moral.** The moral tells a lesson that can be learned. It is revealed at the end of a fable. A moral usually shows how acting in one way is better than acting in another. The moral in this story is underlined. It tells how behaving in one way is better than behaving in another way.

The Wind and the Sun

One day the Wind and the Sun were having an argument. They couldn't agree about who was stronger.

"I'm strong," said the Wind to the Sun.

"So am I," said the Sun.

"Let's have a contest to find out who's stronger," said the Sun. "Can you see that man down there? He's wearing a heavy coat. Let's see who can make him take it off."

"I'll go first," said the Wind. The Wind started to blow. Brrr! The man shivered, but he didn't take off his coat.

The Wind blew harder. It was very cold. The man held onto his hat, and wrapped his scarf around his neck. He kept on walking, and he didn't take off his coat.

"Now it's my turn," said the Sun. The Sun started to shine. The man felt hot, but he didn't take off his coat. He took off his hat and then his scarf. But he kept his coat on.

The Sun shone more brightly. The man felt hotter than ever. At last he stopped walking. He took off his coat.

The Wind knew he was defeated, so he left in a bad mood.

"You are strong, but I'm stronger," called the Sun. "Gently leading is better than a lot of force."

The moral in this fable is that gently leading people to do something is better than forcing them.

Now turn to pages 15–16 to practice recounting a fable.

Name ______________________________

Fable

Practice

Read the fable below.

The Tree and the Reed

A tall tree grew on the bank of a river. The tree was straight and strong. A reed grew next to it. A reed is a plant that is like tall grass. The reed bent when the wind blew.

"Why do you bend so much?" the tree asked.

"Look at me. I am proud of my size. I stand up straight. You should do the same."

"I like being this way," said the reed. "I am not as big as you are, but I am happy."

The next day, a strong wind blew against the tree. The tree tried to keep standing, but its roots came out of the ground. The proud tree fell over.

The wind blew against the reed too. But the reed just bent with the wind until the wind stopped.

Being the biggest and strongest is not always best.

Name ______________________

1. Recount the important events in the order they happened. Write your answers in the chart.

Sequence Chart

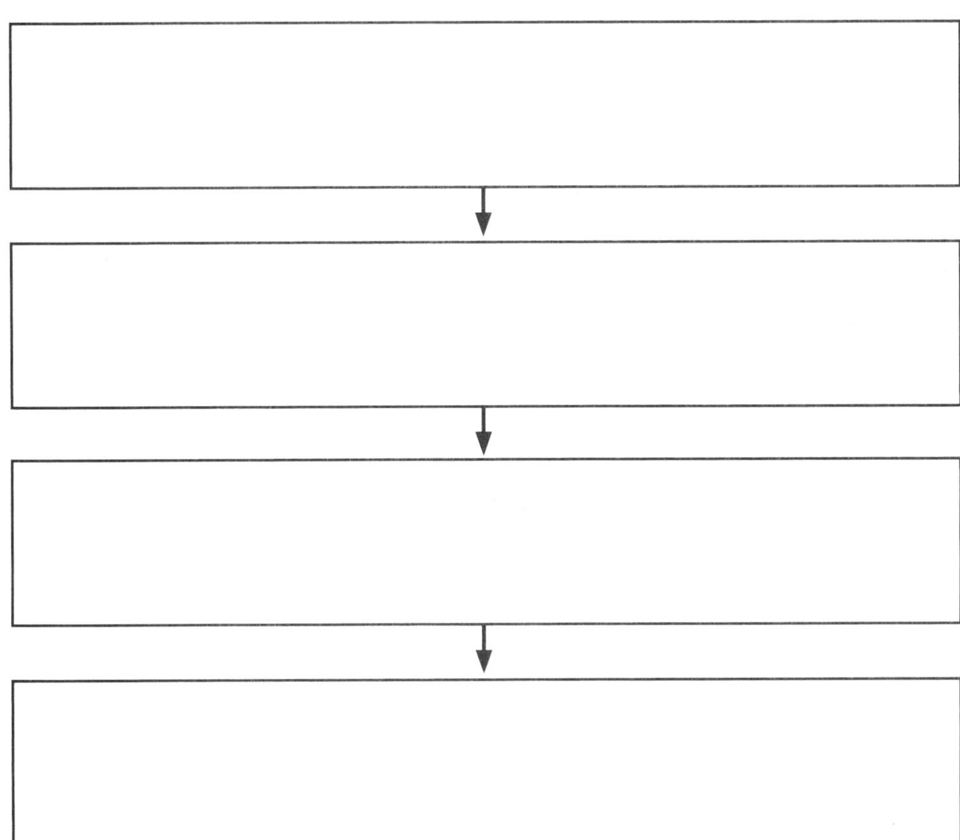

Read the questions. Write your answers on the lines.

2. Why does the tree think he is better?

____

____

3. What is the moral in this story?

____

____

Folktale

A folktale is similar to a fable. It is a short story that has a **message**. A message is like a moral because it also tells a lesson. Folktales are told all over the world. Every culture has these stories to share.

Read the Nigerian folktale.

The Nak Bird and the Odu Bird

A long time ago the king of Calabar wanted to know if there was a bird that could live without eating for long periods. The king said he would make him a chief of his tribe.

Two birds were up to the challenge. The Nak bird and the Odu bird were great friends. They both decided to go before the king and try to be made chiefs. The Nak bird was very small. The Odu bird was much larger. The Odu bird was quite confident that he would win, because he was so much bigger than the Nak bird.

The Odu bird offered to starve himself for seven days. The Nak bird did not say anything, so the king agreed to Odu's plan. He then told both birds to build houses, which he would inspect. Then he would lock them up. The bird that could remain the longest without eating would be made the chief.

They both built their houses. The Nak knew that he could not possibly live for seven days without eating anything. However, he was very tricky. He made a tiny hole in the wall that he could fit through. He covered it up so that the king would not see it. The king came and looked carefully at both houses. He did not see the little hole in the Nak bird's house. So he declared that both houses were safe. He then ordered the two birds to go inside their houses, and the doors were carefully locked on the outside.

Every morning the Nak bird escaped through the opening. He would fly far away and enjoy himself all day. He was careful that no one would see him. When the sun went down he would fly back to his little house. Then he would talk with Odu.

For several days this went on. The voice of the Odu bird grew weaker and weaker every night. At last he could no longer reply to the Nak bird. Then the little bird knew that his friend must have starved. He felt very sorry, but could not tell the king because he was supposed to stay in his house.

When the seven days had passed, the king came and opened both doors of the houses. The Nak bird flew out at once. He rested on a branch of a nearby tree and chirped happily. The king found the Odu bird had starved, just as the Nak bird had thought.

The king appointed the Nak bird to be the head chief of all the small birds. Little did the Nak bird know that by cheating, Nak birds would become the most hunted in all of Calabar.

Today all of the boys in Calabar are given a prize if they manage to catch a Nak bird because of the bird's precious title.

When you **recount** a folktale, you use your own words to tell the important parts, or **plot**, of the story. One way to recount a folktale is to use a sequence chart. In a sequence chart you retell what happened in order from beginning to end.

Sequence Chart

This chart helps you organize the important parts, or plot, of the folktale. You can write the events in the order they happened. If you can't recount the order of events, you can reread the folktale to help you.

SEQUENCE CHART
The king wants to choose a bird that can go long periods without eating to be chief of the tribe.
The Nak bird and the Odu bird agree to the challenge.
The Nak bird cheats and wins the challenge. The Odu bird starves.
The Nak bird is made chief, but now all Nak birds are hunted.

Message

Folktales have a **message**. This message tells a lesson that can be learned. The message usually deals with behaving in a certain way. The underlined part of the story below shows the message.

The Nak Bird and the Odu Bird

A long time ago the king of Calabar wanted to know if there was a bird that could live without eating for long periods. The king said he would make him a chief of his tribe.

Two birds were up to the challenge. The Nak bird and the Odu bird were great friends. They both decided to go before the king and try to be made chiefs. The Nak bird was very small. The Odu bird was much larger. The Odu bird was quite confident that he would win, because he was so much bigger than the Nak bird.

The Odu bird offered to starve himself for seven days. The Nak bird did not say anything, so the king agreed to Odu's plan. He then told both birds to build houses, which he would inspect. Then he would lock them up. The bird that could remain the longest without eating would be made the chief.

They both built their houses. The Nak knew that he could not possibly live for seven days without eating anything. However, he was very tricky. He made a tiny hole in the wall that he could fit through. He covered it up so that the king would not see it. The king came and looked carefully at both houses. He did not see the little hole in the Nak bird's house. So he declared that both houses were safe. He then ordered the two birds to go inside their houses, and the doors were carefully locked on the outside.

Every morning the Nak bird escaped through the opening. He would fly far away and enjoy himself all day. He was careful that no one would see him. When the sun went down he would fly back to his little house. Then he would talk with Odu.

For several days this went on. The voice of the Odu bird grew weaker and weaker every night. At last he could no longer reply to the Nak bird. Then the little bird knew that his friend must have starved. He felt very sorry, but could not tell the king because he was supposed to stay in his house.

When the seven days had passed, the king came and opened both doors of the houses. The Nak bird flew out at once. He rested on a branch of a nearby tree and chirped happily. The king found the Odu bird had starved, just as the Nak bird had thought.

The king appointed the Nak bird to be the head chief of all the small birds. Little did the Nak bird know that by cheating, Nak birds would become the most hunted in all of Calabar.

Today all of the boys in Calabar are given a prize if they manage to catch a Nak bird because of the bird's precious title.

The message is that cheating in order to win has very bad results.

Now turn to pages 24–26 to practice recounting a folktale.

Name ______________________

Folktale

Practice

Read the folktale below.

How the Mockingbird Became the Best Singer

A young mockingbird had a beautiful voice. She wanted to take singing lessons, but she had no money for them.

A young cardinal took singing lessons. Her rich father wanted her to sing. But the young cardinal did not practice. She did not care how she sounded.

The mockingbird hid behind a tree. She watched the singing lessons. She learned how to sing.

The cardinal's father asked the other birds to come and hear his daughter sing. The young cardinal was afraid. She could not sing. She asked a woodpecker to help her cut a hole in the tree. The young cardinal asked the mockingbird to hide there and sing for her.

When the time came to sing, the young mockingbird sang. The young cardinal pretended to sing. The other birds heard a beautiful voice. They all clapped.

The father knew that his daughter was not singing. He found the mockingbird hiding. He told her to come out. "This is the true singer," the father said. "The beautiful voice belongs to the mockingbird."

Name ____________________________

The other birds asked for more music. The mockingbird sang again. Ever since, mockingbirds have had beautiful voices. Cardinals never have learned to sing because they didn't take the time to practice.

1. Recount the important events in the order they happened. Write your answers in the chart.

Sequence Chart

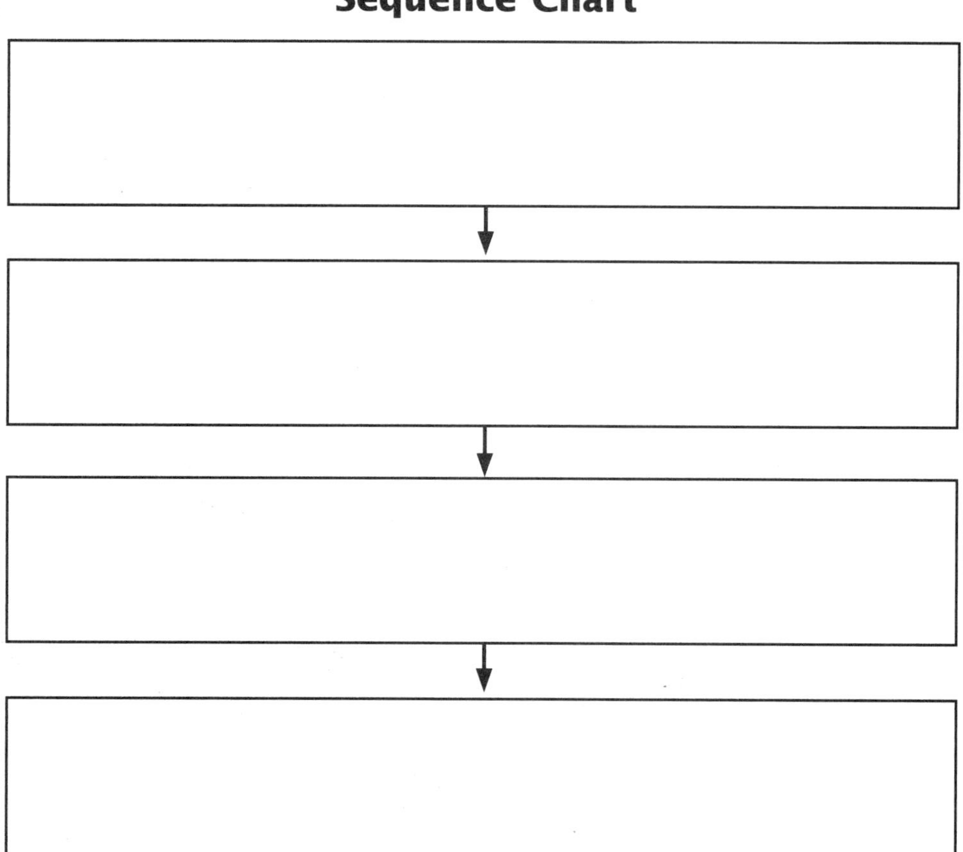

Name ______________________________

Read the questions. Write your answers on the lines.

2. How did the mockingbird learn how to sing?

____

____

3. What is the message in this story?

____

____

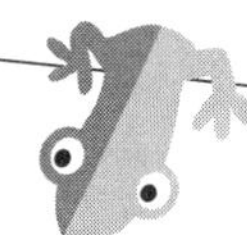

Lesson C

Describe Characters

The **characters** are the people or animals in a story.

Stories are made up of a series of events. These events usually include a problem, or challenge, of some kind. You can understand characters better by describing how they respond to events and challenges in the story.

Look at the **Model** to study characters.

Describe Characters Model

Read the story.

Mr. Jones asked Tessie to take care of his dog Sam. Tessie loved Sam. She smiled and said, "Yes!"

When Mr. Jones left, Sam started howling. Tessie didn't know what to do. She put food in Sam's bowl, but Sam wouldn't eat. She offered Sam a treat, but he wasn't interested. She tried to pet him, but he wouldn't stay still.

Tessie had an idea. She called her best friend, Alexis, who owned a dog. Alexis told Tessie that she should try to take him for a walk. So Tessie took Sam outside for a walk. He stopped howling!

"Good dog!" Tessie said.

Sam gave a happy bark. "Woof!"

With a little bit of thought and hard work, Tessie gave Sam just what he needed.

Who is the main character in this story?

The main **character** in a story usually appears most often.

Tessie appears throughout this story a lot, so you can tell that Tessie is the main character.

What problem does the main character have?

Stories have something called a **plot**. A plot includes a series of **events**. One of those events is a **problem**. A problem is a challenge that the main character faces.

Sam keeps howling. Tessie must get Sam to stop howling. That is the challenge Tessie faces.

1

What is the solution to the problem?

Plots also include a **solution** to a problem. A solution is an answer to a problem. This event shows how the main character responds to challenges.

The solution to Tessie's problem is to take Sam for a walk.

What steps did Tessie take to respond to her challenge?

How a character responds to a challenge says a lot about the character.

At first Tessie tried many ways to get Sam to stop howling. They didn't work. Then Tessie remembered to call a friend who had a dog and she found an answer to the challenge. Tessie was thoughtful and worked hard to make Sam happy.

Now you are ready to practice describing characters and plot. Turn to pages 31–32.

Name ____________________________

Describe Characters

Practice

Read the story below.

It was time to head home from school. Lee could not find his hat. He had seen Jim near the hats and coats earlier. Lee thought Jim took his hat. "You took my hat," Lee said.

Lee was angry. He grabbed his coat to put it on. Then his hat fell out of his own coat pocket. Lee felt bad. "I'm sorry," he said to Jim. "I should have known you wouldn't take my hat. I'll think and look next time before I talk."

Use the key details to help you answer the questions.

1. Who is the main character?

____

2. What problem does the main character have?

____

____

3. How does the main character respond to the problem?

____

____

Name ______________________

4. What is the answer to the problem?

____

____

5. How did the main character respond after the problem is solved?

____

____

Part 1
READING LITERATURE
1.2 Craft and Structure

Standard 4

1

Lesson A

Describe How Words and Phrases Give Meaning and Rhythm

Writers choose their words and phrases carefully. These choices shape the meanings of stories, songs, and poems. These choices can also add rhythm to the stories, songs, and poems.

Rhythm is the patterns of the sounds of the words. Regular beats, alliteration, rhymes, and repeated lines can be used to make rhythmic patterns in text.

In this lesson you'll study models of rhythmic patterns.

Regular Beats

A song can have a regular beat. A regular beat is a rhythmic pattern.

Sing the song "Row, Row, Row Your Boat" silently to yourself.

• • • • •
Row, row, row your boat
• • • • •
Gently down the stream.
••• ••• ••• •••
Merrily, merrily, merrily, merrily,
• • • • •
Life is but a dream.

Row, row, row your boat
Gently down the stream.
Merrily, merrily, merrily, merrily,
Life is but a dream.

Traditional Nursery Rhyme, "Row, Row, Row Your Boat." 1852.

Each syllable in each word is one beat. Look at the dots above the words. These show the number of syllables or beats in each word. For example, the dot above *row* shows it has one syllable, which is one beat. The three dots above *merrily* show that it has three syllables, which are three beats.

Now read about alliteration.

Alliteration

Alliteration is the repeated use of the same beginning sound in a group of words. Here is an example: **A**lice sells **a**pples in **A**tlanta.

Read the poem below. Which sound is repeated at the beginning of many of the words?

Betty Botter
by Mother Goose

Betty Botter bought some butter,
but, she said, the butter's bitter;
if I put it in my batter
it will make my batter bitter,
but a bit of better butter
will make my batter better.
So she bought a bit of butter
better than her bitter butter,
and she put it in her batter
and the batter was not bitter.
So 'twas better Betty Botter
bought a bit of better butter.

1

Alliteration can also be found in stories. Read the end of this story. Look at the last sentence. The words *plants*, *perked*, *pretty*, and *perfect* begin with the *p* sound. The repeated use of the *p* sound gives this sentence a rhythm when you read it.

> Then Tai thought, "Could my plants be thirsty? It was very hot today." He watered his garden. Soon, all his plants perked up, and his pretty garden was perfect again.

Now read about rhymes.

Rhymes

Words that rhyme have the same ending sound. Examples: tall/wall; pound/ground

Some poems contain a rhythmic pattern. Rhyming words may be used at the end of each line, in every other line, or in a different pattern. The pattern brings attention to important words in the poem.

Read the poem.

> One little cat,
> Sat on a mat.
> She did not run,
> She did not pat.
>
> One little frog,
> Sat on a log.
> He did not jump,
> He did not jog.

The words *cat*, *mat*, and *pat* rhyme.
The words *frog*, *log*, and *jog* rhyme.

Both parts of the poem follow the same pattern. The rhyming words are used at the end of the first, second, and fourth lines. This pattern brings attention to what the cat and the frog did and didn't do in the poem.

Now read about repeated lines.

Repeated Lines

Repeated lines give stories and poems a rhythmic pattern.

Read the poem.

The Pelican and the Fish

The fish swims.
The pelican flies over.
The fish swims.
The pelican is hungry.
The fish swims.
The pelican dives down.
The fish swims.

The words "The fish swims" repeat regularly. These words make up every other line of the poem. They give the poem a rhythmic pattern. They also give meaning to the poem.

The pelican is hunting the fish. But the fish keeps swimming. Even in the end the pelican does not get the fish. The fish continues to swim.

Now you have learned about different kinds of rhythmic patterns. Turn to pages 40–42 to practice.

Name ___________________________

Describe How Words and Phrases Give Meaning and Rhythm

Practice

A. Read the poem.

I love it when it's cold and gray.
That is my favorite kind of day.
The wind, it howls, and the rain, it falls.
The hail comes down like bouncing balls.
I can curl up with a book to read.
A cup of cocoa is all I need.
I feel safe and cozy in my bed like a nest.
A cold rainy day is really the best.

1. Circle the words that rhyme.

2. What is the rhyming pattern in the poem?
Tell which lines rhyme.

____

____

Name ______________________________

B. Read the story.

Time to Learn

One day Mama Cat said, "When you were born, you were tiny and could not see. You could not walk. Now you are bigger. Your eyes follow everything that moves. You can run, pounce, climb, and leap. It is time to learn to hunt."

Mama taught her kittens how to hunt mice. She showed them how to sneak slowly and silently. She showed them how to pounce perfectly on their prey.She showed them how to use their claws. Her kittens learned well.

1. Underline two groups of words in the story that show alliteration.
2. How does the alliteration help you picture the kittens?

____

Name ______________________

C. Sing the song silently to yourself.

Mary Had a Little Lamb

Mary had a little lamb, little lamb, little lamb.
Mary had a little lamb whose fleece was white as snow.
Everywhere that Mary went, Mary went, Mary went.
Everywhere that Mary went, the lamb was sure to go.

Hale, Sarah Josepha. "Mary Had a Little Lamb." School Song Book. 1834.

1. Mark the beats above each word in the song with a dot.

2. Underline the repeated phrases in the song.
Does the repetition make the images stronger or weaker? Explain.

____

____

Part 1
READING LITERATURE
1.2 Craft and Structure

Standard 5

1

Lesson B

Parts of Stories

Stories have a beginning, a middle, and an end.

You meet the **characters**, or the people in the story, at the beginning.

At the beginning, you also learn about the **setting**, or where the story happens.

The **plot**, or the action, builds in each part of the story. The plot concludes at the end of the story.

Now look at a model to understand story parts.

Parts of Stories Model

Read the story.

The Rescue

A fierce wind blew over the Texas ranch. Tom and his son Jim looked up at the sky and saw dark clouds gathering. A storm was on its way. They stopped working and put away the tools they had been using to fix the fence.

The two men jumped on their horses to head for home. But Tom knew that they had to check on the cattle first. Tom saw the herd far away. Jim started counting as they rode near. All of the cows were in the group, but Jim could not see all of the calves.

Thunder growled, and lightning flashed. Rain began to pour down from the clouds. Soon Tom and Jim's clothes were soaked.

This time Tom counted. One calf was missing. That calf was too young to be on its own. It belonged with its mother.

Tom rode his horse along the creek. The calf might have been thirsty and wandered off to get a drink. Jim rode in the other direction. At the bank of the creek, Tom saw the missing calf. He called for Jim.

They tied their horses to a nearby tree. Rain had made the path muddy. Tom slipped a little as he made his way to the calf. It was not hurt. He and Jim picked it up and carried it back along the path to safety.

Before long, the calf was beside its mother. Tom and Jim smiled and turned their horses toward home. Soon they would be with the rest of their family, feeling warm and dry.

Now let's learn about characters, setting, and plot. Start with characters.

Characters

Characters are the people who carry out the action in the story. Sometimes animals carry out the action of the story.

- In this story, Tom and Jim are the main characters.
- We meet the characters at the beginning of the story.

Now read about setting.

Setting

The setting is when and where the story takes place.

- The setting is a Texas ranch. The story takes place outside near a creek.
- We learn about the setting at the beginning of the story.

Now read about plot.

Plot

The plot is what happens in the story.

- At the beginning of the story, Tom and Jim notice the storm. They also notice that a calf is missing.
- In the middle of the story, Tom and Jim look for the calf. They find it by the creek. They carry it back to its mother.
- At the end of the story, the calf is safe beside its mother. Tom and Jim ride toward home.

Now that you have learned about characters, setting, and plot, turn to pages 48–50 to practice what you have learned.

Name ______________________________

Parts of Stories

Practice

Read the story.

A Birthday Party for Rabbit

Mouse found Squirrel in the forest. "Squirrel," Mouse called. "Will you help me? I want to have a birthday party for Rabbit."

"Yes," Squirrel said. "What can I do to help?"

"I am not a very good cook," Mouse said. "Can you make a cake for the party?"

They went to Mouse's home. Squirrel made an acorn cake with berries on top. "What else should we do for the party?" asked Squirrel.

"You can draw better than I can," Mouse said. "Will you make Rabbit a birthday card?"

Squirrel folded a piece of paper. He drew red flowers on it. He wrote "Happy Birthday" on it.

"Now we must ask our friends to come," Mouse said. So Squirrel brought Robin and Frog over.

Name ______________________

They said, "Oh, Mouse! You did a very good job!" "Thank you," Mouse said. "I worked very hard." Then Rabbit came in the door.

"Surprise!" they shouted. "Happy birthday, dear Rabbit!" Mouse gave everyone a piece of cake. Then he gave the card to Rabbit.

"Oh, what a pretty card!" she said. "What a good cake! What a nice party! You did a good job, Mouse." She gave Mouse a big hug.

Mouse looked at Squirrel. He thought about Squirrel's help. "Squirrel did the work," he said.

"Thank you, Squirrel! You are a good friend!" Rabbit said.

Answer the questions.

1. Who are the main characters in the story?

____

2. What is the setting of the story?

____

____

Name ______________________

3. Describe the plot of the story. Tell what happens in the beginning, middle, and end.

Beginning:

____

____

Middle:

____

____

End:

____

____

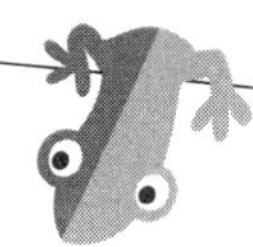

Lesson C

Compare Characters' Points of View

Characters are the people or animals in stories.

- Sometimes the characters have different thoughts and feelings from one another. They have different points of view.
- When you read a story out loud, you can use your voice to show the differences between the characters.

The wolf in "The Three Little Pigs" says, "I'll huff, and I'll puff, and I'll blow your house down!"

- You might use a deep, loud voice when you read the wolf's words.
- This shows that the wolf is big and wants to scare the pigs.

The pigs each say, "Not by the hair of my chinny chin chin!"

- You might use a high, brave voice when you read the pigs' words.
- This shows that the pigs are little but want to stand up to the wolf.

Learn about showing how different characters think and feel. Look at the **Model**.

Characters' Points of View Model

Read a part from a play.

While you read, think about how the different characters think and feel. What is each character's point of view?

Setting: *A city square filled with wrecked carnival stalls. It has been blocked off. Alice, Frasier, and Drew are onstage, looking beyond the "Caution" tape.*

Alice: All that practicing for nothing! The storm has wrecked the carnival. Now there won't be a talent show!

Frasier: Maybe they'll hold the talent show somewhere else.

Drew: How about holding it in the school auditorium?

Frasier: I'm not giving up—I can juggle anywhere. Look!

Drew: That's cool, Frasier! What are you juggling?

Frasier: I'm using socks rolled into balls.

Drew: Are you going to tap dance again, Alice?

Alice: Yes, but I don't want to dance on the school stage. It echoes, and I sound like a horse stamping its feet. That storm has ruined my chances of winning!

How does Alice think and feel about what has happened?

Alice feels gloomy.

- She thinks that there probably won't be a talent show.
- If there is, she thinks she has no chance of winning.

How does Frasier think and feel about what has happened?

Frasier feels hopeful and determined.

- He thinks that they will hold the talent show somewhere else.
- He is not giving up.

How does Drew think and feel about what has happened?

Drew feels hopeful and supportive.

- She thinks the talent show could be held in the school auditorium.
- She tells Frasier that his juggling is cool.

Alice's feelings and thoughts about what has happened are more negative than Frasier's and Drew's. You could say that Alice has a negative point of view.

How can you use your voice to show how Alice feels?

If you read Alice's words out loud, you could use a sad, frustrated voice.

How can you use your voice to show how Frasier feels?

If you read Frasier's words out loud, you could use an excited, determined voice.

How can you use your voice to show how Drew feels?

If you read Drew's words out loud, you could use a happy, friendly voice.

Now you're ready to practice showing how different characters think and feel. Turn to pages 55–56.

Name ______________________

Compare Characters' Points of View

Practice

Read a part from a play.

Setting: *Lunch in the school cafeteria. Tyrone, Jessie, and Natasha turn to one another to discuss the school's new, healthful menu.*

Tyrone: This is a big problem! I'm going to chess club after school. You need to think clearly to play chess. I need brain food!

Jessie: You think that's a problem? I've got tryouts for the swim team this afternoon! I need a big pizza!

Natasha: You'll make it, Jessie.

Jessie: I hope so, but I want to do my best. I want to feel my best. I need food that keeps me going!

Natasha: Maybe this food will be all right. We should just try some.

Tyrone: I don't think so. I want my usual lunch of nachos. If there are no more nachos, I'll have to change schools!

Name ______________________

Now answer the questions.

1. How do Tyrone and Jessie feel about the new menu?

____

____

____

2. How does Natasha feel about the new menu?

____

____

____

3. Use your voice to show how Tyrone and Jessie feel.
Practice with a partner.

Standard 7

Lesson A

Use Illustrations and Words to Understand

Illustrations give you information about what is happening in a story. You can also find words in the story that describe and help you understand the characters, setting, and plot.

In this lesson you will study parts of a story. Start with characters.

Characters

Characters are the people or animals in a story.

Read this page from a story called "Hey, Coach!" Look at the illustrations.

Mom was right. Our next practice was MUCH better. Mom had discovered special drills for each **position**

Chen and Brad were guards. They had to practice dribbling and shooting.

Michael and I were forwards. We **practiced** lay-ups and rebounds.

The characters named on this page of the story are Mom, Chen, Brad, Michael, and the narrator. The narrator is the character speaking. Mom isn't in the illustrations, but you see Chen and Brad dribbling. You also see Michael and the narrator practicing lay-ups and rebounds. The illustrations help you understand basketball practice.

Now read about setting.

Setting

The setting is when and where the story takes place.

Now read these pages from "Hey, Coach!" Look at the illustration.

The setting is the night of the big game. You read this in the first sentence. The illustration shows that the boys are playing on a basketball court.

Now read about plot.

Plot

The plot is what happens in the story.

Now read the last two pages from "Hey, Coach!" Look at the illustration.

Then things started to go **wrong**
Newton was way ahead.

"You're doing great," Mom told us. "Keep it up!"

We dribbled. We rebounded. We made shots. The gap got smaller.

But at the end of the game, we were still one point behind.

We felt bad, but Mom was smiling.

"We're getting better and better!" she said. "Great work, team!"

That made us feel good.

My mom is a **GREAT** coach!

The team was ahead. Now the team is losing to Newton. The boys still played well. But the team lost. Mom said the boys were getting better. This made the team feel good.

The illustration shows Mom talking to the team after the game. The boys look happy even though they lost.

Now you are ready to practice using illustrations and words to understand the characters, setting, and plot of a story. Turn to pages 61–63.

Name ____________________________

Use Illustrations and Words to Understand

Practice

Read the story and look at the illustrations.

A Ride to the Refuge

"We're almost there," Dad said. "I see the sign." He drove into a parking lot and stopped the car. Mom put her bird book into her pocket. She handed Sara a pair of binoculars. "You will see better with these," Mom said.

Sara looked through the binoculars. She saw a sign with a map of Texas. An arrow pointed to a spot on the Gulf Coast. The letters looked big. "What does *refuge* mean?" she asked.

Name ______________________________

"A refuge is a safe place," Mom said. "This is a safe place for birds called whooping cranes."

They climbed onto a bus with other people. As they rode, Sara saw an alligator by the water! Sara saw small birds in the water. Mom looked them up in the bird book. Then everyone looked through their binoculars and saw tall white birds. "There they are!" Mom said. "The whooping cranes are feeding."

Sara watched one bird walk through the water. It poked at something with its bill. It caught a frog!

"We are lucky to see these birds," Dad said. "Not many of them are left."

"I am glad they are safe here," Sara said.

Name ____________________

Answer the questions.

1. Who are the main characters in the story?

____

What do you learn about the characters from looking at the illustrations?

____

____

2. What is the setting of the story?

____

What do you learn about the setting from looking at the illustrations?

____

____

3. What is the plot of the story?

____

____

____

4. How do the illustrations help you understand the plot better?

____

____

____

Lesson B

Compare and Contrast Versions of a Story

Have you ever read a story that seems very familiar?

- Maybe the characters remind you of characters you have met before.
- Maybe the events seem like events you have already experienced.

That's because different authors or people from different cultures often tell the same stories in different ways.

You can compare and contrast different versions of the same story.

- When you **compare** two stories, you tell how they are alike.
- When you **contrast** two stories, you tell how they are different.

Comparing and contrasting different versions of the same story helps you understand important messages about life.

Learn how to compare and contrast different versions of the same story. Look at the **Model**.

Compare and Contrast Versions of a Story: Model

Read the two stories below. The stories are based on tales that have been told for a long time. Different authors tell the stories in different ways.

The Lion and the Mouse

One day, a lion caught a mouse. The lion wanted to eat the mouse for lunch. The mouse squeaked, "Please, big lion. Do not eat me. One day, I may be able to help you!"

The lion said, "You help me? That is so funny, I will let you go."

"Thank you," said the mouse. "I will not forget your kindness."

The next day, the lion was trapped in a net. He could not move. Scared and frustrated, he roared loudly. The mouse came running to help. He chewed the net until the lion was free.

"Thank you, mouse," said the lion. "I think I owe you an apology."

The mouse said, "Now you know a small mouse can help a big lion."

The Dove and the Ant

An ant living in the forest went to the river to get a drink. Nearby, a dove sitting high up in her tree watched the ant. When the ant bent over to drink, she fell in the rushing water.

"Help! The water is moving too fast!" shouted the ant.

Acting fast, the dove picked up a stick and threw it into the river. The ant used the stick to swim to safety.

"I promise to help you one day!" said the ant, catching her breath. The dove didn't take the promise seriously, for how could an ant help a dove?

One day, the ant saw a hunter laying a net for the dove. When the ant stung the hunter's leg, he dropped the net. The ant saved the dove, just as she promised!

"Thank you, friend," said the dove. The ant just smiled.

1

How are these two stories alike?

- First a bigger animal helps a smaller animal.
- Then the smaller animal promises to return the favor.
- The bigger animal doesn't take this promise seriously.
- At the end, the smaller animal saves the bigger animal from a hunter's net.
- The bigger animal learns important lessons about life.

How are these two stories different?

- The first story is about a lion and a mouse. The second story is about a dove and an ant.
- In the first story, the lion decides not to eat the mouse. In the second story, the dove saves the ant from the river.

What do you learn from these stories?

- Specific details in the stories are not important. For example, it doesn't matter if the bigger animal is a lion or a dove.
- What is important is the lesson or lessons the stories help you learn about life. These lessons are:
  "Everyone has the power to help others."
  "If you are kind to others, they will be kind to you."

Now you are ready to practice comparing and contrasting two other versions of the same story. Turn to pages 69–73.

Name ______________________

Compare and Contrast Versions of a Story

What story has wicked stepsisters, a fairy godmother, glass slippers, and a girl who works hard and ends up marrying a prince? *Cinderella!*

You have probably read or heard this story before. The *Cinderella* story is told in many different ways by people from many different cultures.

Practice

Read the two *Cinderella* stories.

Cinderella
An Italian *Cinderella* Story

Once upon a time there was a man who had three daughters. The older daughters were very selfish and bossy. They made their younger sister, Cinderella, do all their work. Cinderella was very kind and never complained. She spent any free time she had taking care of animals.

The father was going on a trip. He asked each one of his daughters to tell what gift they would like him to bring back. The oldest wanted a fancy dress. The other wanted a pretty hat. Cinderella said, "A little bird, please."

Name ______________________

Later, the family was invited to a ball at the king's court. "Cinderella!" her oldest sister said. "If you had asked for a dress, you could have come to the ball with us. You are so foolish!"

When everyone left, Cinderella's bird helped make her beautiful. He gave her a shiny green dress and sparkling glass slippers. She went to the ball, and the king asked her to dance. They danced all night long, until the ball was almost over. "I need to get back home before my family sees I'm gone!" Cinderella said.

She hurried so fast, one of her slippers fell off outside the castle. When she got back home, there was a knock on the door. It was the king! He was holding Cinderella's glass slipper. "It is you!" he said.

Cinderella's family came home just in time to see the king put the slipper on Cinderella's foot. Their mouths fell open in surprise. They opened even wider when the king asked Cinderella to be his wife.

Name ___________________________

Little Ashes
A Native American *Cinderella* Story

Once upon a time, there lived a father and his three daughters. They lived in a wigwam by the side of a lake. The two older sisters were lazy and mean. They made their younger sister tend to the fire and do all the work. This kind girl was called "Little Ashes" because of the soot on her face.

Across the lake, there lived a powerful hero of the tribe. His name was Strong Wind. Strong Wind could make himself invisible. The only person who could see him was his sister, Soft Rain.

Strong Wind wanted to marry. But only a girl with a kind heart could see him and become his wife. The news spread quickly. The older sisters made Little Ashes make them new dresses and beautiful shell belts. They used all the cloth and shells. None were left for Little Ashes.

Sadly, Little Ashes watched her sisters and all the other maidens go to the wigwam where Strong Wind and Soft Rain lived. Then Little Ashes went for a walk in the woods. She saw some pieces of white bark that had fallen from a tree. "I can make a dress of bark!" she thought

Name ___________________________

happily. "Thank you, kind tree!" Then she saw little white and yellow flowers. "I can weave these flowers into a necklace! Thank you, Mother Earth!" she cried.

Meanwhile, all the maidens arrived at Strong Wind's wigwam. Soft Rain asked them if they could see Strong Wind. They all lied and said "yes."

Soft Rain then asked, "By what does my brother pull his sled?" One maiden said a sled, another said a heavy rope, and a third said a dog. But they were all guessing, for they could not see Strong Wind at all.

Just then, Little Ashes stepped forward. She was wearing a simple bark dress and a flower necklace. Soft Rain greeted her kindly and politely.

"Do you see my brother?" Soft Rain asked.

"There is a handsome man coming up the path," answered Little Ashes. "Is he your brother?"

"By what does he pull his sled?" asked Soft Rain.

"By the trunks of two oak trees," Little Ashes answered.

Soft Rain smiled. She had one more question. "What is he wearing?"

Name ____________________________

"He wears a beautiful blanket made of a double rainbow!" said Little Ashes.

Then Strong Wind said, "You do see me! You will be my wife, the light of my life. So I will call you Dawn Light."

With great joy, Strong Wind and Dawn Light were married. Dawn Light's father was happy for his youngest daughter. Her sisters were not.

Now answer the questions.

1. How are these stories alike?

____

____

____

2. How are these stories different?

____

____

____

3. What life lessons do you learn from reading these stories?

____

____

____

Part 2
READING INFORMATIONAL TEXT
2.1 Key Ideas and Details

Standard 1

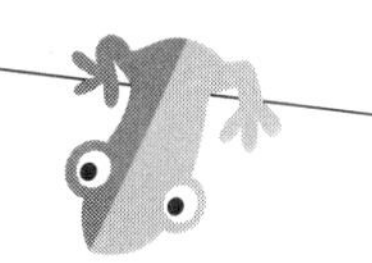

2

Lesson A

Ask and Answer Questions

Good readers ask questions as they read. Sometimes the answers can be found in the selection. Other times readers must use what they already know to answer the question.

Follow these steps when reading:

1. Start with a question word, such as *who*, *what*, *where*, *when*, *why*, or *how*.
2. Think about how you can find the answer.
3. Answer your question.

Look at the **Model** to see how to ask and answer questions as you read.

Ask and Answer Questions Model

Read the selection below.

Pets Rule

Cities need to make rules about pets. Most people have cats and dogs as pets. These pets are easy to take care of. People are safe around them. They don't cause many problems most of the time. However, some people have pets that become a problem for a community.

In Florida a man kept alligators as pets. Neighbors worried about what would happen if the alligators escaped from their pens. The neighbors would not be safe. The town decided that alligators could not be kept as pets. Now the alligators live in a nature preserve. Everybody feels safer.

Now follow these steps.

Ask Questions

What questions do you have about the selection?
Think about *who*, *what*, *where*, *when*, *why*, and *how*.

Here are some questions you might ask to help you understand the selection better.

What kind of pets are safe?

What kind of pets are unsafe?

Why do cities need rules about pets?

Now see how you will find the answers to your questions.

Find Answers

To find the answers to your questions, you can reread, or read again. Look for clues in the selection that will help you answer the questions. The clues are underlined below.

2

1. ***What*** **kind of pets are safe?**

Pets Rule

Cities need to make rules about pets. Most people have cats and dogs as pets. These pets are easy to take care of. People are safe around them. They don't cause many problems most of the time. However, some people have pets that become a problem for a community.

In Florida a man kept alligators as pets. Neighbors worried about what would happen if the alligators escaped from their pens. The neighbors would not be safe. The town decided that alligators could not be kept as pets. Now the alligators live in a nature preserve. Everybody feels safer.

2. *What* kind of pets are unsafe?

Pets Rule

Cities need to make rules about pets. Most people have cats and dogs as pets. These pets are easy to take care of. People are safe around them. They don't cause many problems most of the time. However, some people have pets that become a problem for a community.

In Florida a man kept alligators as pets. Neighbors worried about what would happen if the alligators escaped from their pens. The neighbors would not be safe. The town decided that alligators could not be kept as pets. Now the alligators live in a nature preserve. Everybody feels safer.

3. ***Why* do cities need rules about pets?**

Pets Rule

Cities need to make rules about pets. Most people have cats and dogs as pets. These pets are easy to take care of. People are safe around them. They don't cause many problems most of the time. However, some people have pets that become a problem for a community.

In Florida a man kept alligators as pets. Neighbors worried about what would happen if the alligators escaped from their pens. The neighbors would not be safe. The town decided that alligators could not be kept as pets. Now the alligators live in a nature preserve. Everybody feels safer.

Now use the clues from the text to answer the questions.

Answers

Here are the answers to the questions.

Question: *What* kind of pets are safe?
Answer: Cats and dogs are safe pets.

Question: *What* kind of pets are unsafe?
Answer: Alligators are unsafe pets.

Question: *Why* do cities need rules about pets?
Answer: Some pets, such as alligators, can become a problem for a community.

Now you have asked questions about **key details**. Key details tell more about the main idea of a selection.

Turn to pages 81–82 to practice asking and answering questions.

Name ______________________________

Ask and Answer Questions

Practice

Read the selection.

Sign Language

People who are deaf cannot hear. They need to talk and listen without using sounds. Deaf people communicate in many ways. A language that is often used by deaf people is called sign language.

Sign language uses signs for words. Signs are made using hand shapes and movements. One way of signing is to spell out a word. There is a sign for each letter of the alphabet. Another way to sign is to show a whole word.

Name ____________________

Read the selection again to answer these questions:

- **How do deaf people communicate?**
- **How does sign language work?**

Write your answers.

1. How do deaf people communicate?

____

____

2. How does sign language work?

____

____

3. What is another question you could ask about this selection?

____

____

4. Answer the question you just wrote.

____

____

Part 2
READING
INFORMATIONAL TEXT
2.1 Key Ideas and Details

Standard
2

2

Lesson B

Identify the Main Topic

The **main topic** is what a passage is mostly about. Supporting details tell more about the main topic. Each paragraph also has a focus, or main idea, that supports the main topic.

Look at the **Model** below to see how to identify the main topic.

Identify the Main Topic: Model

Read the passage below.

Have you ever seen a baby squirrel or a baby raccoon? Baby animals are cute. They like to play. Sometimes baby animals are alone. They may seem as though they need help. These are some of the reasons that people want to keep wild animals as pets.

Keeping wild animals as pets can cause problems. Wild animals have special needs. They meet these needs in the places where they live naturally. People can't always meet the needs of a wild animal. Also, wild animals can be dangerous. They can grow large and scratch and bite. They carry diseases too. Wild animals belong in the wild.

Main Idea in a Paragraph

The focus of a paragraph refers to the main idea. To identify the focus of a paragraph, ask yourself: What is the main idea of the paragraph?

- The main idea can usually be found in the first or last sentence of a paragraph. What do you think the main idea of each paragraph is?

The main idea of the first paragraph tells the reasons why people want wild animals as pets.

> Have you ever seen a baby squirrel or a baby raccoon? Baby animals are cute. They like to play. Sometimes baby animals are alone. They may seem as though they need help. These are some of the reasons that people want to keep wild animals as pets.

The main idea of the second paragraph is that keeping wild animals as pets can cause problems.

> Keeping wild animals as pets can cause problems. Wild animals have special needs. They meet these needs in the places where they live naturally. People can't always meet the needs of a wild animal. Also, wild animals can be dangerous. They can grow large and scratch and bite. They carry diseases too. Wild animals belong in the wild.

Now look at the supporting details of each paragraph.

Supporting Details

The supporting details tell more about the main idea.

- Look for details that answer the questions about the main idea of each paragraph.

For the first paragraph, ask yourself: What are the reasons people want to keep wild animals as pets? Clues from the text are underlined below.

> Have you ever seen a baby squirrel or a baby raccoon? Baby animals are cute. They like to play. Sometimes baby animals are alone. They may seem as though they need help. These are some of the reasons that people want to keep wild animals as pets.

These details support the main idea of the first paragraph:

- Baby animals are cute.
- Baby animals like to play.
- Baby animals seem like they need help.

2

For the second paragraph, ask yourself: How does keeping a wild animal as a pet cause problems? Clues from the text are underlined below.

> Keeping wild animals as pets can cause problems. Wild animals have special needs. They meet these needs in the places where they live naturally. People can't always meet the needs of a wild animal. Also, wild animals can be dangerous. They can grow large and scratch and bite. They carry diseases too. Wild animals belong in the wild.

These details support the main idea of the second paragraph:

- People can't meet the special needs of a wild animal.
- Wild animals can be dangerous.
- Wild animals can carry disease.

Main Topic

The main idea of each paragraph supports the main topic of a passage. The main topic of a passage tells the big idea of the passage. To identify the main topic of a passage, ask yourself: What is the big idea in this passage?

- The main topic is usually stated at the beginning or end of a passage. What do you think the main topic of this passage is?

Look at what's underlined below.

> Have you ever seen a baby squirrel or a baby raccoon? Baby animals are cute. They like to play. Sometimes baby animals are alone. They may seem as though they need help. These are some of the reasons that people want to keep wild animals as pets.
>
> Keeping wild animals as pets can cause problems. Wild animals have special needs. They meet these needs in the places where they live naturally. People can't always meet the needs of a wild animal. Also, wild animals can be dangerous. They can grow large and scratch and bite. They carry diseases too. <u>Wild animals belong in the wild.</u>

The main topic of this passage is stated in the last sentence: Wild animals belong in the wild. This means that people should not keep them as pets.

Now turn to pages 88–89 to practice finding the main topic.

Name ______________________________

Identify the Main Topic

Practice

Read the passage below.

Training to be a gymnast requires a lot of time and effort. The morning routine is tough. Children begin with stretches at 6:30 in the morning! Next they go into classrooms. That is where they are taught reading, math, and other lessons until lunchtime. There is a lot to remember.

The afternoon routine is also hard. After lunch the younger students take a nap. Then training goes on until dinnertime! Sometimes the children perform the same exercise for an hour. They only stop when they do it right. Children finally rest at the end of the day. The next day starts the same routine again.

Name ______________________________

Find the main idea and supporting details of each paragraph. Then find the main topic of the entire passage.

1. What is the main idea of the first paragraph?

____

____

2. What is the main idea of the second paragraph?

____

____

3. Circle or underline two supporting details in the first paragraph.

4. Circle or underline two supporting details in the second paragraph.

5. What is the main topic of the entire passage?

____

____

Standard 3

2

Lesson C

Read Historical Text

The word *history* means "important things that happened in the past." **Historical text** tells facts and information about important events that happened in the past.

The historical events you read about are often **connected**, or related. Sometimes one event causes another. This is called **cause** and **effect**. A cause is why something happens. An effect is what happens.

Clue words or phrases are words that tell you about cause and effect. Some clue words that tell you about cause and effect include *because*, *so*, and *since*.

Look at the **Model** to see one way that historical events can be connected.

Read Historical Text: Model

Read the passage below. The clue phrase is underlined.

> Memphis became a city in 1849. The land was good for growing things, so many farmers moved to Memphis to grow cotton.
>
> The city started to get bigger. A disease called yellow fever spread through Memphis in the 1870s. <u>As a result</u>, thousands of people died. Many people left the city, but later came back.

2

Look at the phrase *as a result*. The word *result* means "something that happens because of something else."

Now ask: What happened?

Then ask: Why did this happen?

The answers to these questions will show you cause and effect.

What happened?

> A disease called yellow fever spread through Memphis in the 1870s. As a result, thousands of people died.

- Thousands of people died. This is what happened. It is the effect.

Why did it happen?

> A disease called yellow fever spread through Memphis in the 1870s. As a result, thousands of people died.

The cause should answer *why* the effect happened.

- The cause is that a disease called yellow fever spread through Memphis. This is *why* thousands of people died.

Now you are ready to describe connections in historical text. Turn to page 93 to practice.

Name ____________________________

Read Historical Text

Practice

Read the passage below.

In 1849, public schools weren't very common in Oregon. As a result, laws were passed to set up a free public school system. Oregon's first free public school opened in 1851. Because the population grew, more schools were built. Gradually schools opened throughout Oregon. Today the state has many high schools and elementary schools.

Write your answers on the lines.

1. Find one clue word or phrase in the selection that tells you about cause and effect.

____

2. Write one example of cause and effect from this selection. Tell the cause, and then tell the effect related to it.

Cause:

____

____

Effect:

____

____

Standard 3

2

Lesson D

Read Scientific Text

Scientific text tells about science. It tells about facts, ideas, and concepts.

The scientific concepts you read about are often **connected**, or related. You can describe the **connections** between concepts. One way is to **compare** and **contrast** the information.

Look at the **Model** to see one way that scientific concepts can be connected.

Read Scientific Text: Model

Read the passage below.

Many animals today are similar to animals from long ago. For example, the woolly mammoth lived long ago. Today the elephant looks like a woolly mammoth. But woolly mammoths were even bigger than elephants! Like elephants, woolly mammoths had tusks and a trunk. Unlike elephants, they had long, shaggy hair all over their bodies. Their long hair kept them warm. Woolly mammoths lived during the Ice Age when it was very cold.

When you compare information, you tell how it is alike.

- Ask yourself: How are elephants like woolly mammoths? Use the information in the passage to help you.
  - Elephants look like woolly mammoths looked.
  - Elephants have tusks and a trunk like woolly mammoths had.

2

When you contrast information, you tell how it is different.

- Ask yourself: How are elephants different from woolly mammoths?
  Use the information in the passage to help you.
  - Elephants are smaller than woolly mammoths.
  - Elephants don't have long, shaggy hair over their bodies. Woolly mammoths did.
  - Elephants are around today. Woolly mammoths lived during the Ice Age.

Now you are ready to describe connections in scientific text. Turn to page 97 to practice.

Name ______________________

Read Scientific Text

Practice

Read the passage below.

Tornadoes and hurricanes both have strong winds. They both cause a lot of damage. They have differences too.

Hurricanes begin over warm oceans. Tornadoes usually begin over land. A hurricane can stretch for hundreds of miles, but a tornado rarely stretches more than one mile. Hurricanes last for many hours. Tornadoes usually last under an hour.

Because they are so dangerous, people need to find safe shelter in both hurricanes and tornadoes.

Write your answers on the lines.

1. List two ways that hurricanes and tornadoes are alike.

____

____

2. List two ways that hurricanes and tornadoes are different.

____

____

____

____

Standard 3

2

Lesson E

Read Technical Text

Some texts give information. One kind of text that gives information is **technical text**.

- Some technical texts might tell about an important topic.
- Other technical texts might give directions about how to make or do something.
- Many technical texts have pictures that help you understand what you read.

Directions are steps that tell you how to make or do something.

Directions are one kind of technical text.

If you understand how the steps in directions are connected, you will know what to do and why.

Look at the **Model**.

Read Technical Text: Model

Read the directions and look at the picture.

How to Make a Bird Feeder

1. Rinse an empty plastic milk jug until it is clean.
2. Have an adult help you use scissors to cut a hole in the middle of the jug. Make the hole almost as wide as the jug. (The hole must be big enough for a bird to fly through.)

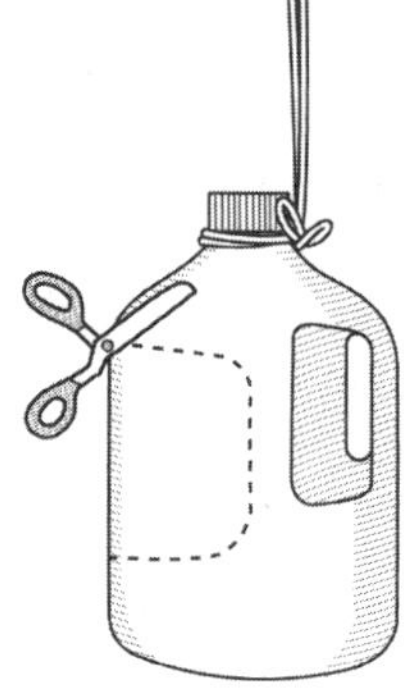

3. Leave the bottom of the jug on. (The seeds will go inside the jug.)
4. Tie string around the neck of the jug.
5. Pour the seeds in.
6. Tie the loose end of the string to a tree branch.
7. Watch the birds eat!

2

What task do these directions tell you how to do?

These directions tell you how to make a bird feeder.

How do you know when to do the steps?

- Sometimes the steps in directions are numbered. Sometimes the steps have sequence words, such as *first*, *then*, *next*, and *last*.
- As you can see, the steps in these directions are numbered so you know when to do them.

What should happen *before* you cut the hole?

You should rinse a plastic milk jug until it is clean.

What should happen *as* you cut the hole?

You should make the hole almost as wide as the jug so that a bird can fly through.

What should happen *after* you cut the hole?

You should tie string around the neck of the jug. Then you should fill the feeder with seed and tie it to a tree branch.

What would happen if you skipped Step 3?

If you skipped Step 3, there would be nowhere to put the seed.

How do the pictures help you understand what to do?

- The first picture shows how big to make the hole and how much space to leave at the bottom of the jug.
- The second picture shows how much seed to use and how to hang the feeder.

Now you are ready to practice describing how the steps in directions are connected. Turn to pages 102–104 to practice.

Name ______________________

Read Technical Text

Practice

Read the directions.

How to Make a Bookmark

1. Decide how long and how wide you want your bookmark to be.
2. On poster board or cardboard, draw a rectangle that is the size you want your bookmark to be. Use a ruler to make sure that you get the sides straight.
3. Use scissors to cut out your bookmark.
4. At one end of the bookmark, make a hole with a hole punch.

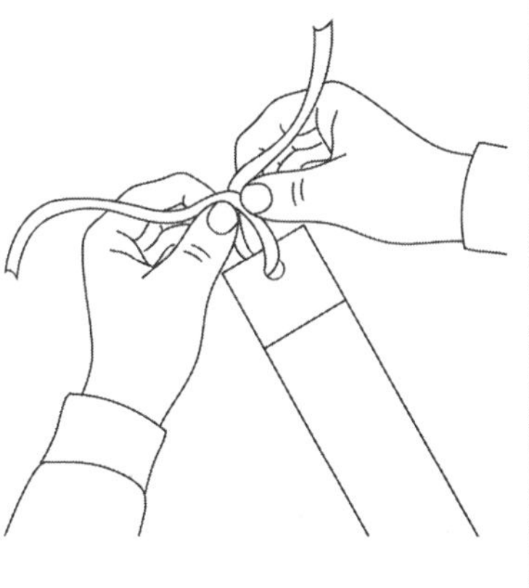

5. Measure and cut a piece of ribbon that is six inches long.
6. Thread the ribbon through the hole and tie it in a double knot.
7. Use colored pencils or markers to decorate your bookmark.

Name ______________________________

Now answer the questions.

1. What task do these directions tell you how to do?

____

____

2. How do you know when to do the steps?

____

____

3. What should happen *before* you draw the bookmark?

____

____

4. What should happen *as* you draw the bookmark?

____

____

5. What should happen *after* you draw the bookmark?

____

____

6. What might happen if you skipped Step 5?

7. How does the picture help you understand what to do?

Part 2
READING
INFORMATIONAL TEXT
2.2 Craft and Structure

Standard 4

2

Lesson A

Learn the Meanings of New Words and Phrases

If you find a word you don't know when you read, use context clues to figure out what the word means.

To use context clues, look at the other words and sentences nearby for hints about what the word means. Ask how the other words or sentences might help you understand the new word.

Look at the **Model** to learn how to figure out new words when you are reading a story or reading about another subject.

Learn the Meanings of New Words and Phrases: Model

Read the paragraph below.

Pete's family kept a special book. The book had hundreds of pages. It had information about the family's ancestors. Pete learned a lot about his family from the book. He found out that some ancestors had come over on the Mayflower. Later, other ancestors had traveled to Kansas. They had established farms there. They made their living on the farms they started. His ancestors used the money to buy more land. Still other family members had settled in California.

Ancestors is a hard word. Reread these two sentences to find clues about the meaning of the word *ancestors.*

It had information about the family's ancestors.

Pete learned a lot about his family from the book.

- Pete learned about his family from the book.
- The book had information about his ancestors.
- Ancestors must be family members who lived long ago.

Established is also a difficult word.
Look at these sentences for clues
about what *established* means.

> They had established farms there.
> They made their living on the farms they started.

- The two sentences tell how Pete's family started farms.
- Established must mean "started."

But what does the phrase *made their living* mean?

Look for clues in these sentences.

> They made their living on the farms they started.
> His ancestors used the money to buy more land.

- Pete's ancestors made money working on the farm.
- The phrase *made their living* means "to make money or earn enough to live."

Now you are ready to practice using context clues and asking and answering questions to understand words or phrases you don't know.

Turn to pages 108–109 to practice.

Name ____________________

Learn the Meanings of New Words and Phrases

Practice

Read the paragraph below.

Australia is an arid continent. It is the driest continent in the world. It has ten deserts.

All deserts are very dry. Many are hot during the day and cold at night. But plants and animals have adapted to life in the desert. They have made changes that allow them to live there.

The red kangaroo lives in the Australian desert. A female carries its young in a pouch, or pocket, on its stomach. Kangaroos need very little water. They rest during the heat of the day and eat at night. Red kangaroos graze on grasses and plants.

Australia is an interesting continent!

Name ______________________________

Use context clues and ask and answer questions to figure out the meaning of the underlined words.

Write the meanings of the words on the lines.

1. arid:

____

____

2. adapted:

____

____

3. pouch:

____

____

4. graze:

____

____

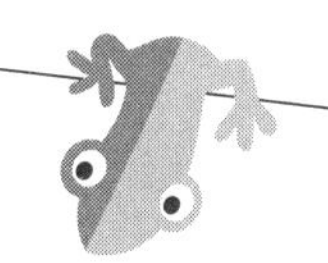

Lesson B

Locate Facts and Information

You can read to find facts and information. Sometimes you read books. Other times you use a computer to read information on the Internet.

In this lesson you will learn more about finding facts and information. Start with text features.

Text Features

Text features help you find information in a book. They also help you understand what you are reading. Captions, bold print, subheadings, glossaries, and indexes are examples of text features.

Now study different text features. Start with captions.

Captions

Look at this page from a book.

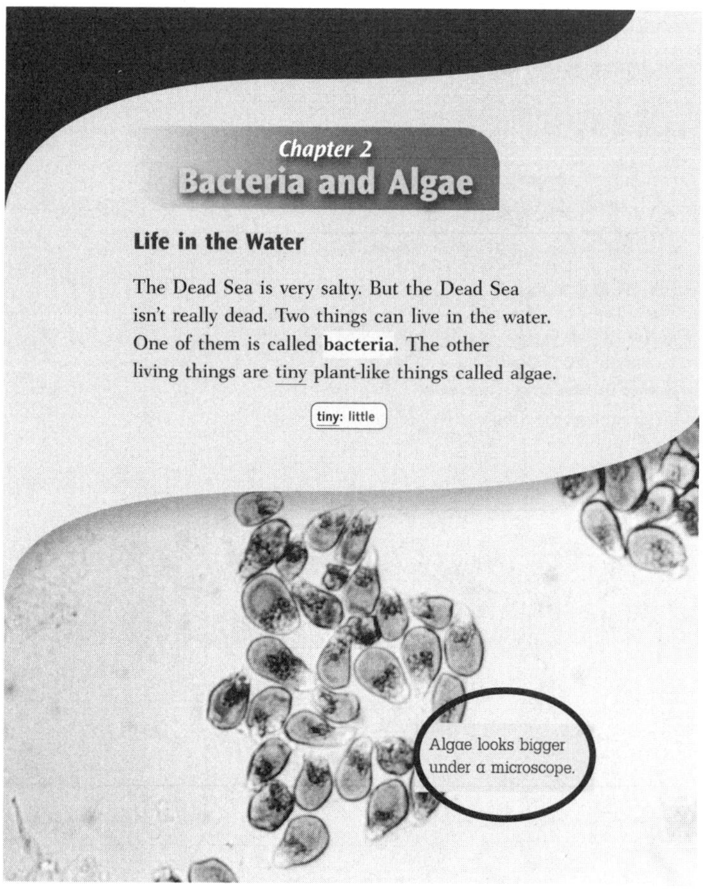
Chapter 2
Bacteria and Algae

Life in the Water

The Dead Sea is very salty. But the Dead Sea isn't really dead. Two things can live in the water. One of them is called **bacteria**. The other living things are tiny plant-like things called algae.

tiny: little

Algae looks bigger under a microscope.

The sentence "Algae looks bigger under a microscope" is a caption.

A caption tells you information about a photograph or picture.

By reading the caption, you know that the photograph is of algae under a microscope.

Now read about bold print.

National Geographic/Getty Images

Bold Print

Look at the highlighted word *bacteria* in the fourth sentence below.

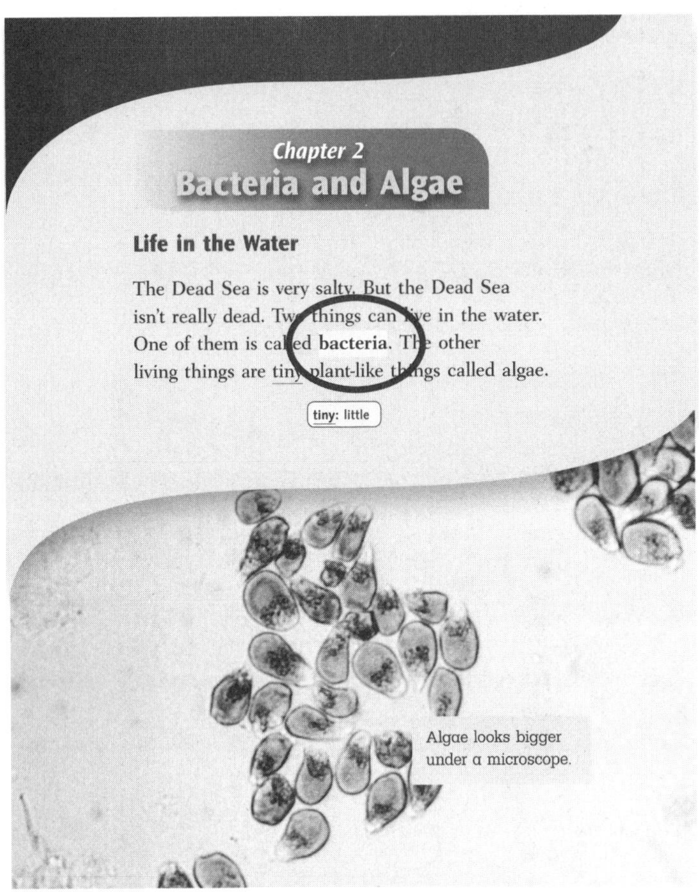

The word *bacteria* is in bold print. Bold print is used to call attention to something important.

Here *bacteria* is an important word.

Knowing words in bold print helps you understand the passage better.

Now read about subheadings.

National Geographic/Getty Images

Subheadings

A subheading is a title that tells what you will read next. A subheading gives more detailed information than a chapter heading.

Look at the page below.

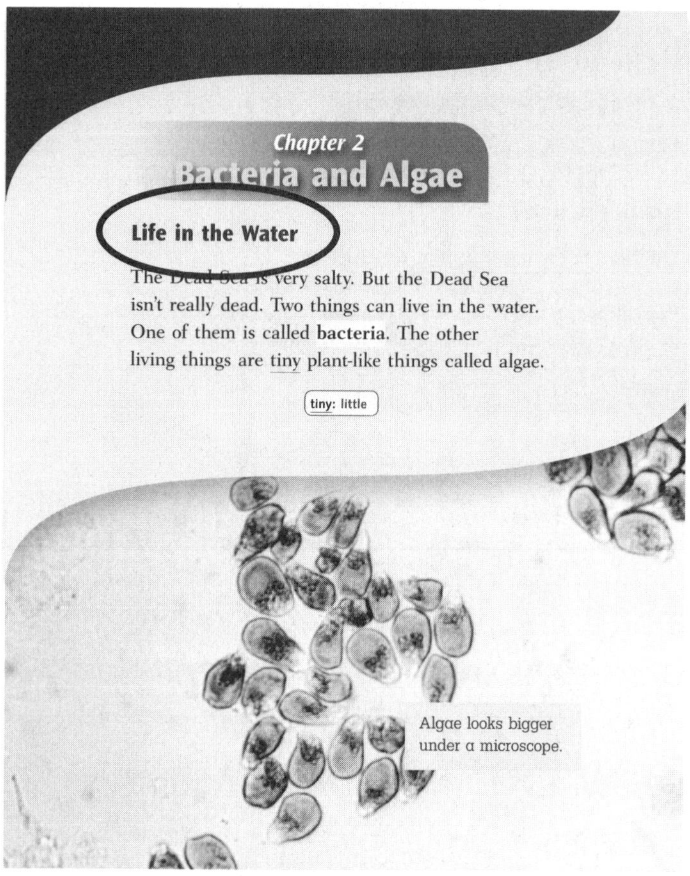

The title "Life in the Water" is a subheading. The chapter heading is "Bacteria and Algae." The subheading gives more information about bacteria and algae. You know bacteria and algae live in water before you start reading.

Now read about glossaries.

National Geographic/Getty Images

Glossaries

A glossary gives the meaning of words in a selection.

Look at the page below.

Notice the highlighted word *bacteria.*

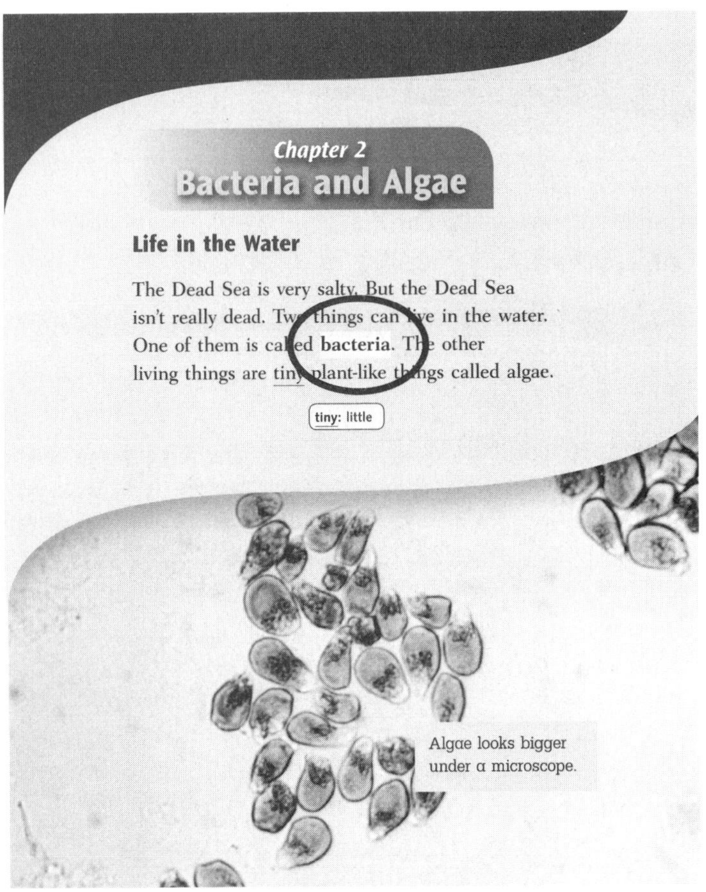

National Geographic/Getty Images

Now look at this page. This is the Glossary. The Glossary is found in the back of the book.

You can find the meaning of the word *bacteria* here. You also learn how to pronounce the word and its part of speech. The number tells you on which book page you will find this word.

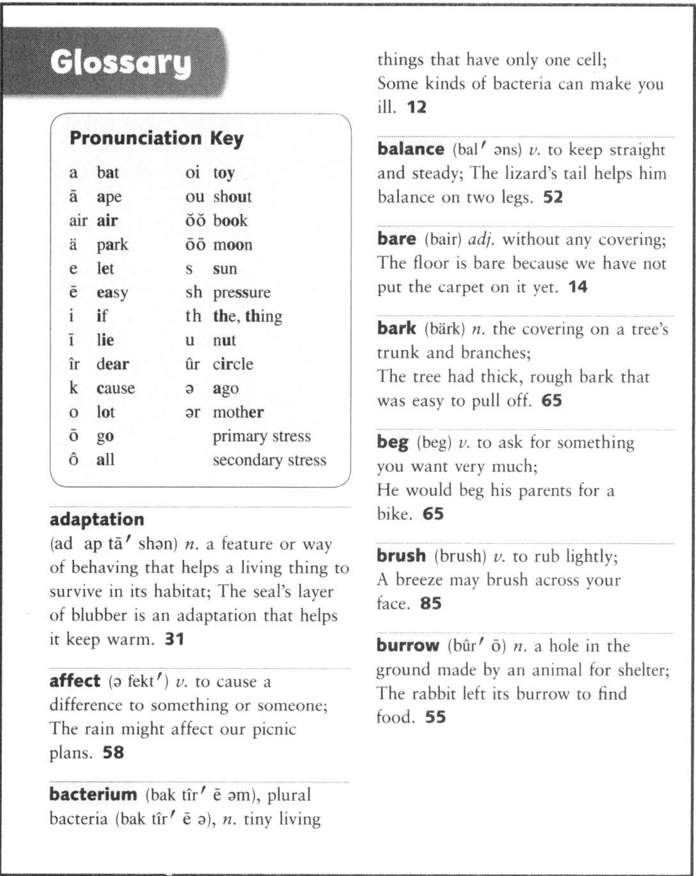

Glossary

Pronunciation Key

a	bat	oi	toy
ā	ape	ou	shout
air	air	ŏŏ	book
ä	park	ōō	moon
e	let	s	sun
ē	easy	sh	pressure
i	if	th	the, thing
ī	lie	u	nut
îr	dear	ûr	circle
k	cause	ə	ago
o	lot	ər	mother
ō	go		primary stress
ô	all		secondary stress

adaptation (ad ap tā′ shən) *n.* a feature or way of behaving that helps a living thing to survive in its habitat; The seal's layer of blubber is an adaptation that helps it keep warm. **31**

affect (ə fekt′) *v.* to cause a difference to something or someone; The rain might affect our picnic plans. **58**

bacterium (bak tîr′ ē əm), plural bacteria (bak tîr′ ē ə), *n.* tiny living things that have only one cell; Some kinds of bacteria can make you ill. **12**

balance (bal′ əns) *v.* to keep straight and steady; The lizard's tail helps him balance on two legs. **52**

bare (bair) *adj.* without any covering; The floor is bare because we have not put the carpet on it yet. **14**

bark (bärk) *n.* the covering on a tree's trunk and branches; The tree had thick, rough bark that was easy to pull off. **65**

beg (beg) *v.* to ask for something you want very much; He would beg his parents for a bike. **65**

brush (brush) *v.* to rub lightly; A breeze may brush across your face. **85**

burrow (bûr′ ō) *n.* a hole in the ground made by an animal for shelter; The rabbit left its burrow to find food. **55**

Bacteria is the plural word for bacterium. Read the definition given for bacterium to understand what bacteria are.

Now read about indexes.

Indexes

This page shows the index for a book.

Index

An index lists words alphabetically. It also lists page numbers. You can use the words to find facts about each topic listed. If you want to know about algae, look under A for algae. Facts about algae are on pages 12 and 13 in the book.

You have studied the different text features. Now study search tools.

Use Search Tools

Search tools help you find information on a computer.

You can type in a keyword to tell the search engine what information to look for. For example, you might want to learn about ant farms. You could enter "ant farm" as the keyword.

Another way to find information on a computer is by using pictures or symbols called icons. Clicking on an icon lets you see information.

On a computer, an icon can take you to the table of contents.

When you click on an icon, new information is displayed.

2

Practice using an **icon** to find information. When you click the icon, it takes you to the table of contents so you can locate information on the Web site.

1. Type in your *Common Core State Standards Literacy eHandbook* address into your browser's address bar.
2. Click on Part 2 Reading: Informational Text in the first Table of Contents.
3. Go to 2.2 Craft and Structure in the second Table of Contents.
4. Click on Lesson B Locate Facts and Information.
5. Click on Use Search Tools.
6. Click on Home to practice using an icon.

Now you have studied different text features and search tools. Turn to pages 119–123 to practice.

Name ______________________

Locate Facts and Information

Practice

**Follow these directions to view a book page.
Then answer the question about a caption.**

- Type in your *Common Core State Standards Literacy eHandbook* address into your browser's address bar.
- Click on Part 2 Reading: Informational Text in the first Table of Contents.
- Go to 2.2 Craft and Structure in the second Table of Contents.
- Click on Lesson B Locate Facts and Information.
- Click on Use Search Tools.
- Click on Practice.
- Click on **caption**.

1. This image shows an example of a caption.
Read the caption. What is the image of?

____

Name ______________________________

Follow these directions to view a book page.
Then answer the question about print.

- Type in your *Common Core State Standards Literacy eHandbook* address into your browser's address bar.
- Click on Part 2 Reading: Text in the first Table of Contents.
- Go to 2.2 Craft and Structure in the second Table of Contents.
- Click on Lesson B Locate Facts and Information.
- Click on Use Search Tools.
- Click on Practice.
- Click on **bold print**.

2. The highlighted word is an example of bold print. Read the word in bold print. Why is this word important?

____

____

Name ______________________

Follow these directions to view a book page.
Then answer the question about a subheading.

- Type in your *Common Core State Standards Literacy eHandbook* address into your browser's address bar.
- Click on Part 2 Reading: Informational Text in the first Table of Contents.
- Go to 2.2 Craft and Structure in the second Table of Contents.
- Click on Lesson B Locate Facts and Information.
- Click on Use Search Tools.
- Click on Practice.
- Click on **subheading**.

3 The word below the chapter banner is an example of a subheading. What is the subheading? What will you read about in the passage?

____

____

Name ______________________

**Follow these directions to view a book page.
Then answer the question about a glossary.**

- Type in your *Common Core State Standards Literacy eHandbook* address into your browser's address bar.
- Click on Part 2 Reading: Informational Text in the first Table of Contents.
- Go to 2.2 Craft and Structure in the second Table of Contents.
- Click on Lesson B Locate Facts and Information.
- Click on Use Search Tools.
- Click on Practice.
- Click on **glossary**.

4. This image shows an example of a glossary.
What is the meaning of the word *beg*? On which page of the book could you find this word?

____

____

Name ______________________________

Practice

**Follow these directions to view a book page.
Then answer the question about an index.**

- Type in your *Common Core State Standards Literacy eHandbook* address into your browser's address bar.
- Click on Part 2 Reading: Informational Text in the first Table of Contents.
- Go to 2.2 Craft and Structure in the second Table of Contents.
- Click on Lesson B Locate Facts and Information.
- Click on Use Search Tools.
- Click on Practice.
- Click on **index**.

5. This image shows an example of an index.
On what pages can you find information about moose?

____

Standard 6

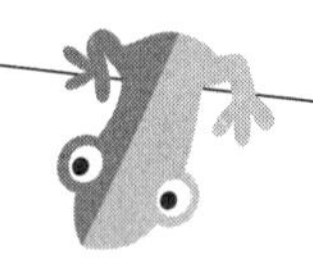

2

Lesson C

Identify Text Purpose

A writer's reason for writing is called the **author's purpose**.

Authors have different purposes for writing. Authors may write to inform readers, to entertain readers, or to persuade readers to agree.

When an author's purpose is to inform readers, the author might

- answer a question or explain something.
- describe a person, place, or thing.

Learn how to identify the author's purpose in a selection. Look at the **Model**.

Identify Text Purpose: Model

Read the selection below.

Have you ever seen a giant parade balloon? You might have seen one that looks like your favorite cartoon character. It takes work to turn a cartoon character into a giant balloon. First, an artist draws a picture to show what the balloon will look like. Next, other artists make a model of the balloon out of clay. Then they make a second model and paint it. Finally, other workers cut pieces of material. These pieces are the parts of the balloon. They are sealed together with heat. At last, the giant balloon is ready to fly high in the sky!

2

What is the author's purpose?

To identify the author's purpose, ask yourself three questions.

1. What is the topic of this selection, or what is this selection about?
   - The topic of this selection is giant parade balloons.
2. What information does the author give about this topic?
   - The author says that it takes work to turn a cartoon character into a giant parade balloon.
   - The author tells about each step in the process of making a giant parade balloon.
3. What does this information tell about the author's purpose?
   - This information tells that the author's purpose is to explain. The author is writing to explain why it takes work to make a giant parade balloon.

Let's read another selection.

A sandy beach is a great place to be on a summer day. You can smell suntan lotion and feel crunchy sand under your feet. When the sun beats down on the beach and it is really hot, the sand feels like fire! Then you can hop into the water to cool off. Sometimes you can see tiny fish, pretty shells, and colorful stones in the water. If it is not too hot, you can splash and play in the ocean and taste the salt water. When the weather forecaster says it is going to be warm and sunny, pack up and head to the beach!

2

What is the author's purpose?

To identify the author's purpose, ask yourself those three questions again.

1. What is the topic of this selection, or what is this selection about?
   - The topic of this selection is the beach.
2. What information does the author give about this topic?
   - The author says that the beach is a great place to be on a summer day.
   - The author tells about all the things you can smell, feel, see, and taste at the beach.
3. What does this information tell about the author's purpose?
   - This information tells that the author's purpose is to describe. The author is writing to describe what it is like to be at the beach on a warm summer day.

Now you are ready to practice identifying the author's purpose in a selection. Turn to page 129.

Name ____________________________

Identify Text Purpose

Practice

Read the selection.

We have a huge, old tree in our backyard. In the spring and summer, it is covered in bushy clumps of sweet-smelling green leaves. I like to lean against its rough, brown trunk and sit in the cool shade. In the fall, the leaves turn a lovely tone of yellow. They glitter like gold in the sunlight and rustle in the wind. In winter, the tree is bare. I can see the big branches twist high up into the blue sky. I love my tree because it is beautiful all year round.

Now answer the questions.

1. What is this selection about?

____

2. What information does the author give you?

____

____

____

3. Based on this information, what is the author's purpose?

____

2

Lesson A

Understand and Use Visual Information

Informational text is nonfiction text. Nonfiction text uses words and visuals to give the reader facts. Pictures are visuals. Charts, diagrams, and graphs are also visuals. Using visuals helps you understand information more quickly than words alone.

In this lesson you will learn more about charts, diagrams, and graphs. Start with charts.

Charts

A chart is one way to organize information. Information is organized under headings. It is often easier to read facts in a chart than in a paragraph.

Read the paragraph.

Did you know that some plants can grow in a pond? Like all plants, pond plants need air, sunlight, and water to grow. Water lilies are one kind of pond plant. Water lilies have big, broad leaves that float on top of the water. These big leaves use sunlight to make food and help the plant grow. Most pond plants, like the water lily, have roots to get water. Roots can also hold the plant in place. Water lilies also have flowers. These flowers make seeds. The seeds go to the bottom of the pond. Each seed can grow into a new water lily plant.

2

Now look at the chart.

Features of the Water Lily		
	Feature	**Purpose**
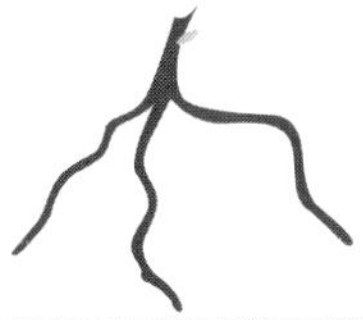	**Root**	Holds plant in place
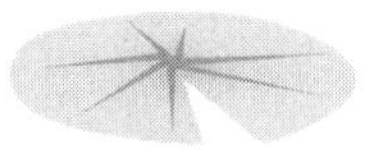	**Leaf**	Makes food for plant
	**Flower**	Helps make seeds
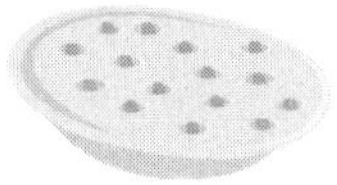	**Seed**	Grows into new plant

There are a lot of facts about pond plants in the paragraph. It is easier to remember the important facts by organizing them into a chart. You can quickly see what each part of the water lily does.

Now you are ready to practice using charts. Turn to pages 133–134.

Name ______________________________

Charts

Practice

Read the paragraph.

Look in the Sonoran Desert at night. You might find a Desert Spadefoot Toad. Toads are amphibians. They can live on the land or in the water. Deserts are often dry. To protect itself, the Desert Spadefoot Toad goes underground. It has short front and back legs. It is also a gray or brown color with a pale belly. It can hide easily in the sandy soil. It stays cool here until night. At night, this nocturnal animal eats insects. Then in the summer, when it rains, the Desert Spadefoot Toad lays eggs.

Look at the chart.

Desert Spadefoot Toads		
Where They Are Found	Characteristics	Other Facts
Sonoran Desert	olive gray to brown color	eat insects
underground	pale belly	nocturnal
on land or in water	short limbs	lay eggs
	amphibian	

Name ____________________

Use the paragraph and chart to answer the questions.

1. Where can you find a Desert Spadefoot Toad?

____

____

2. What colors can Desert Spadefoot Toads be?

____

____

3. When do Desert Spadefoot Toads eat?

____

What do they eat?

____

4. How does the chart help you understand the paragraph?

____

____

____

Diagrams

A diagram is a drawing that gives information. Looking at a diagram helps you understand what you are reading.

Read the paragraph.

> Penguins have two kinds of feathers. They have soft feathers next to their skin. These feathers trap body heat. Penguins have stiff feathers on the outside. These feathers keep out the wind and water.

Now look at the diagram.

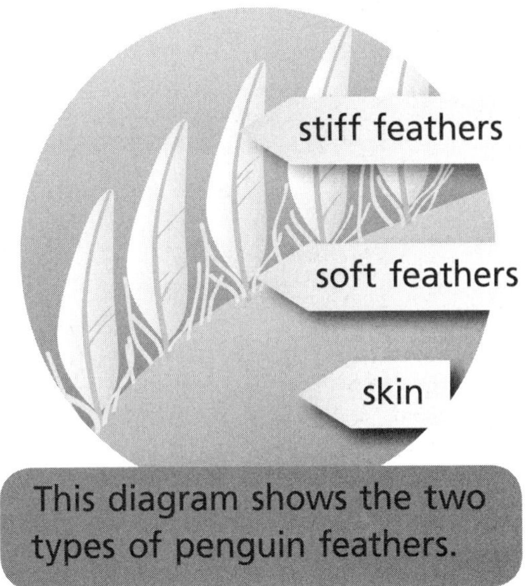

This diagram shows the two types of penguin feathers.

The text and diagram tell about penguins' feathers. The diagram shows where the feathers are and how they look. You can better understand how penguins keep warm in the cold by seeing the diagram of the feathers.

Now you are ready to practice using diagrams. Turn to pages 137–138.

Name ______________________________

Diagrams

Practice

Read the paragraph.

A pine tree has many parts that keep it healthy and growing. Pine trees need food and water. The roots take water from the soil. The trunk and branches carry the water to other parts of the tree. The needles make food for the tree. The needles stay green all year. Pine trees also have cones. Cones hold the tree's seeds. When the cones drop the seeds, more pine trees begin to grow in the ground.

Look at the diagram.

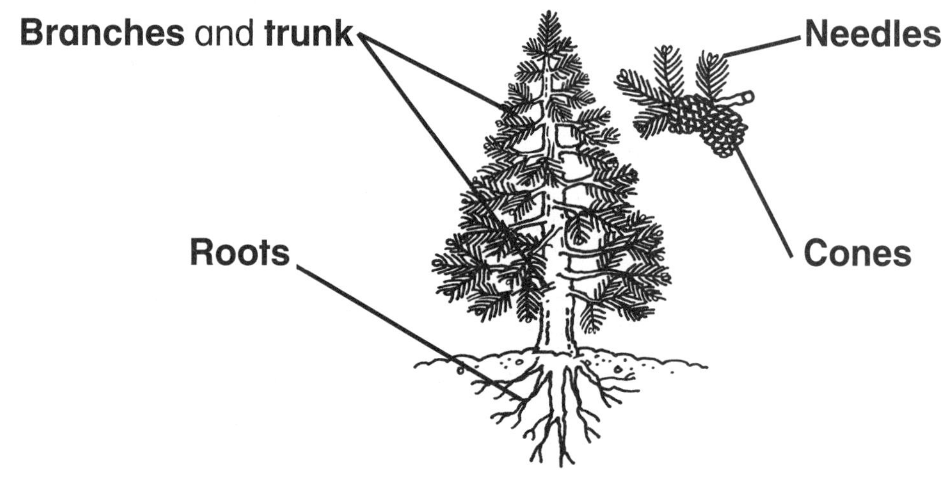

Name ______________________

Answer the questions.

1. What are the parts of a pine tree?

____

____

2. What do the roots do?

____

____

3. How do the roots, trunk, and branches work together?

____

____

____

4. How does the diagram help you understand the paragraph?

____

____

____

Graphs

A graph presents information visually. There are circle graphs, line graphs, and bar graphs. Each kind of graph shows the relationship between two or more things.

Read the paragraph.

Governments give us many services, but what do they want in return? Governments need money. They can't help us if they can't hire and pay workers. Governments need a lot of money to build schools and hire teachers. Governments also buy equipment such as garbage trucks and machines to fix roads. Your family pays taxes to governments. These taxes help governments pay for what they need.

2

Now look at the circle graph.

Planned Government Spending
New York State (2011)

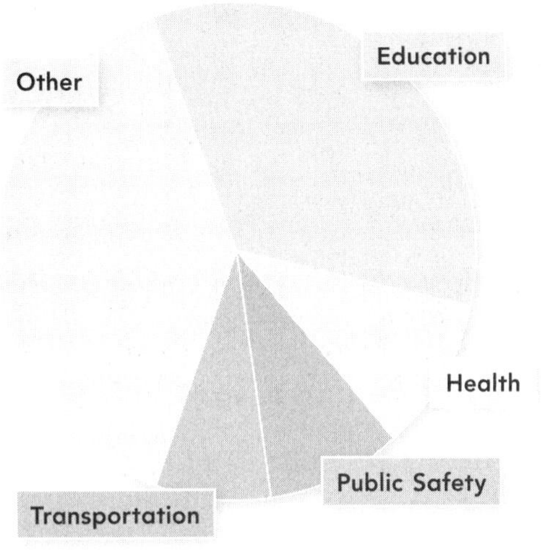

Area of Spending

Education (staff, new schools, books)

Health (staff, new buildings, equipment)

Public Safety (police, firefighters)

Transportation (roads, buses)

Other (water, waste, streetlights)

The circle graph helps you understand what governments spend their money on. More money is spent for the areas that take up the larger parts of the circle. For example, not as much money is spent on transportation as is spent for education.

Now you are ready to practice using graphs. Turn to pages 141–142.

Name ______________________

Graphs

Practice

Read the paragraph.

A farmer had five hens laying eggs for two weeks. There was a sixth hen that was not laying eggs. Each of the hens was given the same amount of food and water each day. Not all the hens laid the same number of eggs.

Look at the bar graph.

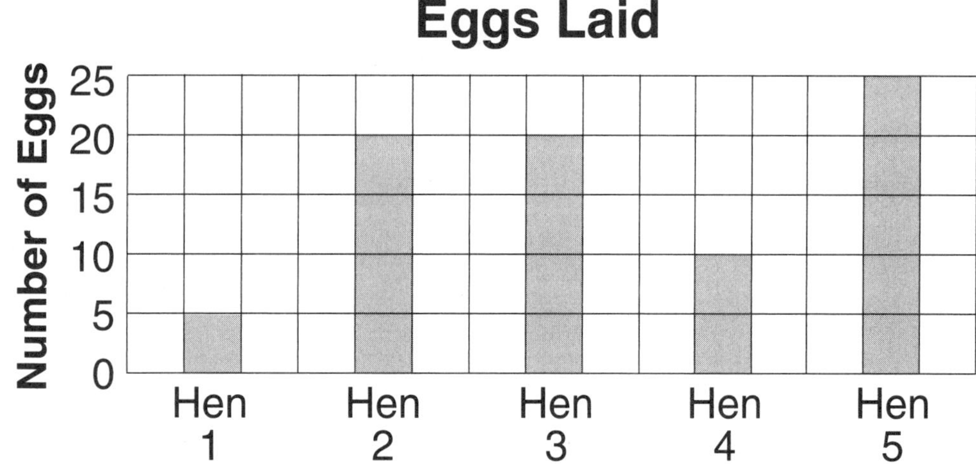

Name ______________________________

Answer the questions.

1. How many eggs did Hen 4 lay?

____

2. Which hens laid the same number of eggs?

____

3. Which hen laid the lowest number of eggs?

____

4. Why doesn't the graph show how many eggs the sixth hen laid?

____

____

Part 2
READING
INFORMATIONAL TEXT
2.3 Integration of Knowledge and Ideas

Standard 8

2

Lesson B

Describe How Reasons Support Key Points

A selection has key points, or main ideas, the author wants to share.

Authors sometimes give **reasons** to support the main ideas.

- These reasons explain why the main ideas make sense.
- These reasons support the author's main message.

Learn how to describe the way reasons support the main ideas in a selection. Look at the **Model**.

Describe How Reasons Support Key Points: Model

Read the selection below.

Texas is home to the elf owl. In some ways, the elf owl is like other owls. It hunts at night. It also eats insects, mice, lizards, and other small birds.

In many other ways, the elf owl is very special. The elf owl is one of the smallest owls in the world. It grows to only about six inches long. Another interesting thing about the elf owl is how it protects itself. When the elf owl thinks it is in danger, it hides under its wing or "plays dead." Unlike many other owls, the elf owl likes to live in homes made by other birds. You will find the elf owl nesting in the old home of a woodpecker in a cactus stalk, tree limb, or wooden pole or post.

Main Idea in Paragraph 1

Ask yourself: What is the main idea in Paragraph 1?

The main idea in Paragraph 1 is underlined below.

> Texas is home to the elf owl. In some ways, the elf owl is like other owls. It hunts at night. It also eats insects, mice, lizards, and other small birds.

The main idea in Paragraph 1 is that the elf owl is like other owls in some ways.

The author states the main idea near the beginning of the paragraph.

Reasons

Ask yourself: What reasons does the author give to support this main idea?

The reasons the author gives to support this main idea are underlined below.

> Texas is home to the elf owl. In some ways, the elf owl is like other owls. It hunts at night. It also eats insects, mice, lizards, and other small birds.

The author gives two reasons to support the main idea in Paragraph 1:

- The elf owl hunts at night.
- The elf owl eats insects, mice, lizards, and other small birds.

These reasons explain why the elf owl is like other owls in some ways.

Main Idea in Paragraph 2

Ask yourself: What is the main idea in Paragraph 2?

The main idea in Paragraph 2 is underlined below.

> In many other ways, the elf owl is very special. The elf owl is one of the smallest owls in the world. It grows to only about six inches long. Another interesting thing about the elf owl is how it protects itself. When the elf owl thinks it is in danger, it hides under its wing or "plays dead." Unlike many other owls, the elf owl likes to live in homes made by other birds. You will find the elf owl nesting in the old home of a woodpecker in a cactus stalk, tree limb, or wooden pole or post.

The main idea in Paragraph 2 is that the elf owl is very special in many other ways.

The author states the main idea near the beginning of the paragraph.

Reasons

Ask yourself: What reasons does the author give to support this main idea?

The reasons the author gives to support this main idea are underlined below.

> In many other ways, the elf owl is very special. The elf owl is one of the smallest owls in the world. It grows to only about six inches long. Another interesting thing about the elf owl is how it protects itself. When the elf owl thinks it is in danger, it hides under its wing or "plays dead." Unlike many other owls, the elf owl likes to live in homes made by other birds. You will find the elf owl nesting in the old home of a woodpecker in a cactus stalk, tree limb, or wooden pole or post.

The author gives three reasons to support the main idea in Paragraph 2:

- The elf owl is one of the smallest owls in the world.
- The elf owl "plays dead" to protect itself.
- The elf owl likes to live in homes made by other birds.

These reasons explain why the elf owl is special in many other ways.

Now you are ready to practice describing how reasons support main ideas. Turn to pages 150–151.

Name ______________________________

Describe How Reasons Support Key Points

Practice

Read the selection below.

Today, there are thousands of farms across the United States. But most people don't live near farms. The food has to travel to reach them.

In the past, food did not travel far from farms. Travel took a long time. There were no roads, only bumpy dirt trails. And the only way to get around was with a wagon pulled by a horse.

Then things began to change. New roads were built. Steamboats appeared on the rivers. Railroad trains were introduced. Many towns and cities were connected. Now food could travel farther from the farms.

Now answer the questions.

1. Circle the main idea in Paragraph 2.
2. Underline three reasons the author gives to support this main idea.

Name ____________________________

3. How do these reasons support this main idea?

____

____

____

4. Circle the main idea in Paragraph 3.
5. Underline three reasons the author gives to support this main idea.
6. How do these reasons support this main idea?

____

____

____

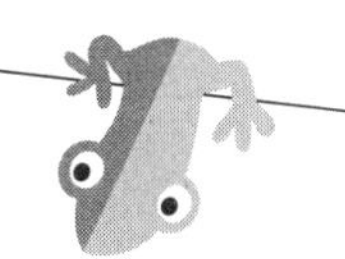

2

Lesson C

Compare Multiple Sources

Sometimes you might read two selections about the same topic. For example, you might read two selections about life in the Arctic.

Each selection will have key points, or main ideas, the author wants to share about life in the Arctic.

- You can **compare**, or tell what is alike about the main ideas in the two selections.
- You can **contrast**, or tell what is different about the main ideas in the two selections.

Telling what is alike and different about the main ideas will help you better understand the topic of life in the Arctic.

Learn to tell what is alike and different about the main ideas in two selections. Look at the **Model**.

Compare Multiple Sources: Model

Read two selections about the cactus.

Selection 1

The desert can be hot and dry. It can be a difficult place for many plants to survive, but not for the cactus!

A cactus can survive quite well in the desert because of a special ability. It can store its own water! It has waxy skin that keeps the water inside the plant.

This skin is an adaptation. An adaptation is a special part or way of acting that helps a plant or animal survive. The waxy skin of the cactus lets the plant store water to use when there is no rain.

Selection 2

A desert is a dry habitat. It is a good home for a plant like the cactus, which does not need much water to live.

Not only can a cactus find a good home in the desert, it helps animals live there, too. Flowers grow on the cactus. These flowers have nectar that birds and bats can drink.

The cactus also provides homes for some animals. Some birds use sticks to make nests on the cactus. Other birds dig holes in the cactus and use the holes for nests.

How are main ideas in Selections 1 and 2 alike?

See what's underlined below.

Selection 1

The desert can be hot and dry. <u>It can be a difficult place for many plants to survive, but not for the cactus!</u>

A cactus can survive quite well in the desert because of a special ability. It can store its own water! It has waxy skin that keeps the water inside the plant.

This skin is an adaptation. An adaptation is a special part or way of acting that helps a plant or animal survive. The waxy skin of the cactus lets the plant store water to use when there is no rain.

2

Selection 2

A desert is a dry habitat. It is a good home for a plant like the cactus, which does not need much water to live.

Not only can a cactus find a good home in the desert, it helps animals live there, too. Flowers grow on the cactus. These flowers have nectar that birds and bats can drink.

The cactus also provides homes for some animals. Some birds use sticks to make nests on the cactus. Other birds dig holes in the cactus and use the holes for nests.

Look at the underlined passages in both selections. As you can see, the selections begin with main ideas that are **alike**.

Both selections tell that the desert is a good place for a cactus.

How are main ideas in Selections 1 and 2 different?

See what's underlined below.

Selection 1

The desert can be hot and dry. It can be a difficult place for many plants to survive, but not for the cactus!

A cactus can survive quite well in the desert because of a special ability. It can store its own water! It has waxy skin that keeps the water inside the plant.

This skin is an adaptation. An adaptation is a special part or way of acting that helps a plant or animal survive. The waxy skin of the cactus lets the plant store water to use when there is no rain.

2

Selection 2

A desert is a dry habitat. It is a good home for a plant like the cactus, which does not need much water to live.

Not only can a cactus find a good home in the desert, it helps animals live there, too. Flowers grow on the cactus. These flowers have nectar that birds and bats can drink.

The cactus also provides homes for some animals. Some birds use sticks to make nests on the cactus. Other birds dig holes in the cactus and use the holes for nests.

Look at the underlined passages in both selections. As you can see, the two selections go on to tell about main ideas that are **different**.

- Selection 1 explains why the cactus can survive in the desert.
- Selection 2 explains how the cactus helps animals survive in the desert.

Now you are ready to practice telling what is alike and different about main ideas in two other selections. Turn to pages 159–160.

Name ____________________________

Compare Multiple Sources

Practice

Read two selections about seahorses.

Selection 1

The ocean is a huge saltwater habitat. It is a good habitat for a unique type of fish called a seahorse.

The seahorse has special body parts that help it survive in the ocean. It has a long snout. This snout can suck in many small organisms, or living things, that float by. Seahorses eat a lot!

The sea horse also has small fins on its back and head that help it swim. If the ocean current is too strong, the seahorse can curl its tail around coral and other plants. This helps the seahorse take a rest or just stay in one place.

Selection 2

The ocean is a huge and wonderful place. It is a good home for one of the most unique kinds of fish in the world: the seahorse!

Name ______________________

The seahorse is unique for several reasons. For example, a pair of sea horses can link tails and swim side by side. What is most unusual about the seahorse, though, is that the male has babies! A male sea horse has a pouch in front of his body. He carries the eggs in his pouch until they hatch. Then many tiny seahorse babies swim out into the water!

Now answer the questions.

1. Tell how a main idea in Selection 1 and a main idea in Selection 2 are alike.

____

____

____

2. Tell how a main idea in Selection 1 and a main idea in Selection 2 are different.

____

____

____

Part 3
READING:
FOUNDATIONAL SKILLS
3.1 Phonics and Word Recognition

Standard
3

Lesson A

Phonics

In English there are twenty-six letters of the alphabet that can be combined in many different ways to make words. In order to read and write, we must know all the ways these letters can be put together to make different sounds. In this lesson you will learn more about phonics.

3

Distinguishing Long and Short Vowel Sounds

There are long and short vowel sounds.
The words below have long vowel sounds.

Long A	tape
Long E	theme
Long I	fine
Long O	hope
Long U	cute

To hear the differences between
short and long vowel sounds,
remember these rhymes:

A's my name.
Two sounds I make:
Short *a* in *lamb*,
Long *a* in *rake*.

E's my name.
Two sounds for me:
Short *e* in *hen*,
Long *e* in *he*.

I's my name.
Two sounds have I:
Short *i* in *pig*,
Long *i* in *fly*.

O's my name.
Two sounds I know:
Short *o* in *stop*,
Long *o* in *go*.

U's my name.
Two sounds I use:
Short *u* in *cub*,
Long *u* in *fuse*.

Read the words below to help you hear the difference between short and long vowel sounds.

/a/ and /ā/	pan	pane	ran	rain
/e/ and /ē/	deck	deep	head	heel
/i/ and /ī/	bit	bite	hid	hide
/o/ and /ō/	hop	hope	sock	soak
/u/ and /ū/	mud	mule	fuss	fuse

Now turn to page 164 to practice distinguishing long and short vowels.

3

Name ______________________

Distinguishing Long and Short Vowel Sounds

Practice

Read each heading. Write the words on the lines under the correct heading.

eve	reach	flash	class	pine
pin	grow	pan	pet	slope
mule	tail	rust	breath	stop

Short Vowel Words	Long Vowel Words
______________	______________
______________	______________
______________	______________
______________	______________
______________	______________
______________	______________
______________	______________
______________	______________

Vowel Team Sound/Spellings

These words have long vowel sounds.

Long A	late
Long E	theme
Long I	time
Long O	bone
Long U	mule

One way to spell a long vowel sound is by using two vowels together to say one long sound. This is called a **vowel team**.

Common Vowel Teams		**Examples**	
Long A	ai_, _ay	t**ai**l	d**ay**
Long E	ee, ea	sw**ee**t	d**ea**l
Long I	_ie, _igh	t**ie**	r**igh**t
Long O	_ow, oa_	l**ow**	fl**oa**t
Long U	_ew, _ue	f**ew**	stat**ue**

Now turn to pages 166–167 to practice long-vowel teams.

Name ____________________________

Vowel Team Sound/Spellings

Practice

Read each sentence. Write the word on the line that correctly completes each sentence.

1. Can you ______________ what you said?

a. reapeat b. repeat c. repet

2. The teacher will ______________ the assignment.

a. explain b. explaine c. explane

3. Did you see the black ______________ fly away?

a. crow b. crowe c. croa

4. Max turned on the ______________ so he could see better.

a. lite b. liet c. light

5. My sister and I sometimes ______________ over books.

a. argu b. argue c. argew

6. We like to ______________ kickball at recess.

a. playe b. plai c. play

7. Emma ______________ her shoes tightly.

a. tied b. tighted c. tie

Name ______________________________

8. Did the bank ______________ you some money?

a. lown b. lone c. loan

9. The talent show is only two ______________ away.

a. weaks b. weeks c. wecks

10. Alice has a niece and a ______________.

a. nephew b. nephue c. nefew

Decoding Two-Syllable Words

One way to read a word is to break it into parts called **syllables**. Each syllable must have a vowel sound. To count the number of syllables in a word, count the number of vowel spellings.

One-Syllable Words	Two-Syllable Words
made	paper
ride	spider
deep	secret
clock	broken
huge	tutu

Now read the word *beyond*.
Remember that each syllable has a vowel sound/spelling. There is a *v*, for vowel, under each vowel spelling in *beyond*.

beyond
v v

Next, notice that the letter between the vowels is a consonant and has a *c*, for consonant, under it.

beyond
vcv

When you see a vowel-consonant-vowel spelling pattern, you usually divide the word before the consonant spelling.

be/yond
v/cv

3

Look only at the first syllable.
When there is a vowel spelling
that is not followed by a consonant spelling,
the vowel is usually long. This is called
an **open syllable**. Blend the first syllable: be.

Then blend both syllables and read
the word: beyond.

Remember, if a word has a vowel-consonant-vowel
spelling, you can divide the word after the first vowel.
But this will not work with every word. After you
read a word, ask yourself, "Does it sound right?"
or "Does it make sense?"

Now turn to pages 171–172 to practice
reading two-syllable words.

Name ______________________

Decoding Two-Syllable Words

Practice

Choose the word that completes each sentence.
Write the word on the line.

1. A ______________ has eight legs and makes a web.
a. spider b. sliding

2. Antoine likes to ______________ he is a king.
a. provide b. pretend

3. Grandpa picked a ______________ for me.
a. depart b. daisy

4. My class is reading a ______________ about a frog that can talk.
a. fable b. favor

5. Mr. Baker will ______________ me in math.
a. tutu b. tutor

6. My best friend lives in the house ______________ mine.
a. beside b. basic

7. Another name for a student is ______________.
a. pupil b. pieces

Name ______________________

8. Can you ____________ what you said?

a. repair b. repeat

9. The ____________ steers the plane through the sky.

a. pilot b. photo

10. Anna's ____________ sister sleeps in her crib.

a. behind b. baby

Decoding Words with Prefixes and Suffixes

A **prefix** is a word part that is added to the beginning of a base word to make a new word. Some common prefixes are:

Prefix	Meaning	Example
dis-	"not" or "opposite"	dislike
un-	"not"	unkind
mis-	"bad," "wrong," or "incorrectly"	misprint
mid-	"middle"	midnight

A **suffix** is a word part that is added to the end of a base word to make a new word. Some common suffixes are:

Suffix	Meaning	Example
-er	"one who"	singer
-ness	"the state of being"	darkness
-ly	"in a certain way"	slowly
-y	"full of"	rainy
-ed	changes the verb tense	stopped
-less	"without"	careless
-ful	"full of"	joyful

3

When a base word contains a short vowel followed by a consonant, the consonant is usually doubled before adding the suffix *-ed*.

A prefix or a suffix often adds a syllable to the base word. Say the word *painless* syllable by syllable and clap for each syllable you hear: pain/less - 2 syllables.

Now turn to pages 175–178 to practice reading words with prefixes and suffixes.

Name ______________________________

Decoding Words with Prefixes and Suffixes 1

Practice

A. Add the prefixes to the base words below. Write the new word on the first line. Then write the meaning of the new word.

	Prefix	Base Word	New Word	New Meaning
1.	dis-	agree	________________	____________________________
2.	mis-	place	________________	____________________________
3.	un-	locked	________________	____________________________
4.	mid-	week	________________	____________________________
5.	dis-	trust	________________	____________________________
6.	un-	stuck	________________	____________________________
7.	mid-	morning	________________	____________________________
8.	mis-	behave	________________	____________________________

Name ______________________________

B. Choose the word that completes each sentence. Write the word on the line.

1. Did I ________________ your directions to the game?

a. misunderstand b. disunderstand

2. Mr. Collins does not like ________________.

a. unhonesty b. dishonesty

3. Cooper used a key to ________________ the door.

a. midlock b. unlock

4. It is easy to ________________ when you have a lot of items.

a. discount b. miscount

5. I get in trouble when I ________________ my parents.

a. unobey b. disobey

6. We have a ________________ recess break at school.

a. midmorning b. mismorning

7. It is ________________ for me to be sick.

a. unusual b. disusual

8. The employee worked on his ________________ review.

a. unyear b. midyear

Name ______________________________

Decoding Words with Prefixes and Suffixes 2

Practice

A. Add the suffixes to the base words below. Write the new word on the first line. Then write the meaning of the new word.

	Suffix	Base Word	New Word	New Meaning
1.	-ly	nice	______________	__________________________
2.	-er	surf	______________	__________________________
3.	-y	dirt	______________	__________________________
4.	-ness	sad	______________	__________________________
5.	-less	care	______________	__________________________
6.	-ful	fear	______________	__________________________

B. Add the suffix *-ed* to the base words below. Make sure to double the final consonant.

	Present Tense		Suffix		Past Tense
1.	nod	+	ed	=	______________
2.	swat	+	ed	=	______________
3.	skip	+	ed	=	______________

Name ______________________

C. Choose the word that completes each sentence. Write the word on the line.

1. Write your name ______________ on the paper.

a. neatly b. neatness

2. Miguel ______________ the car at the red light.

a. stopped b. stoped

3. Mia made ______________ mistakes on her spelling test.

a. careful b. careless

4. The tiger ______________ shouted his commands.

a. trained b. trainer

5. My baby sister gets ______________ when she is hungry.

a. fussy b. fussed

6. Tyrell has a ______________ for bananas.

a. fondness b. fondful

7. Logan's broken leg was ______________.

a. painless b. painful

8. Lily ______________ the blanket around her body.

a. wrapped b. wrapping

Spellings with Inconsistent Sounds

There are some spelling patterns that have different sounds. In order to read and understand these words, you may have to ask yourself, "Does it sound right?" or "Does it make sense?"

Read the following words and sentence aloud. Listen to the different sounds of the spelling pattern *ough* in the words: line 1 /ō/; line 2 /u/; line 3 /aw/. Notice that when the letter *t* is added to the end of *ough*, the spelling pattern makes the /aw/ sound.

Line 1	dough	though
Line 2	tough	rough
Line 3	bought	sought

Sentence 1 Arnell **bought enough** supplies to make **dough** for dinner.

3

Another spelling that has different sounds is *oo*. These letters can represent two sounds, /ü/ as in *goo* and /u̇/ as in *book*. Read the following words and sentences aloud. Listen to the different sounds of the spelling pattern *oo* in the words.

Line 1 good brook

Line 2 smooth shampoo

Sentence 1 Sue **took** a picture of the **pool**.

Sentence 2 I **stood** near the **raccoon** at the **zoo**.

There are even more spelling patterns that represent two sounds:

Spelling Pattern	Sound 1	Sound 2
ow	/ō/ as in *row*	/ow/ as in *town*
_*ew*	/ū/ as in *few*	/ü/ in *new*
_*ue*	/ū/ as in *rescue*	/ü/ as in *true*

Now turn to pages 181–183 to practice spellings with inconsistent sounds.

Name ______________________________

Spellings with Inconsistent Sounds 1

Practice

blue	flew	rookie	hue
shallow	true	crowded	nephew
view	yellow	rescue	football
booth	groomer	new	eyebrows

Write the words with the *ow* spelling pattern under the correct sound, /ō/ or /ow/.

/ō/	/ow/
1. ______________________	1. ______________________
2. ______________________	2. ______________________

Write the words with the *oo* spelling pattern under the correct sound, /ü/ or /oo/.

/ü/	/oo/
1. ______________________	1. ______________________
2. ______________________	2. ______________________

Write the words with the _*ew* spelling pattern under the correct sound, /ū/ or /ü/.

/ū/	/ü/
1. ______________________	1. ______________________
2. ______________________	2. ______________________

Name ____________________________

blue	flew	rookie	hue
shallow	true	crowded	nephew
view	yellow	rescue	football
booth	groomer	new	eyebrows

Write the words with the *_ue* spelling pattern under the correct sound, /ū/ or /ü/.

/ū/	/ü/
1. ________________	**1.** ________________
2. ________________	**2.** ________________

Name ______________________________

Spellings with Inconsistent Sounds 2

Practice

Circle the correct word to complete each sentence.

1. Jasmine (brought, bough) her tent on the camping trip.
2. (Althought, Although) I live close to the school, I still ride the bus.
3. I (though, thought) the homework was due tomorrow.
4. Do we have (enough, enought) seats for everyone?
5. Kendall used the (dought, dough) to bake bread.
6. Jude (bough, bought) a present for her grandma.
7. The prince (fought, fough) the dragon and won.
8. The pirate (sought, sough) the treasure using a map.

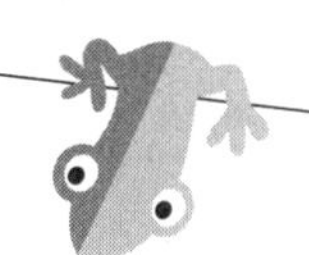

Lesson B

High-Frequency Words

- **High-frequency words** are words you see a lot in books.
- These words are important to recognize and to understand.

Name ______________________

High-Frequency Words

Practice

1. Cut out the words.
2. Look for words you know.
3. Ask a partner or teacher about words you do not know.
4. Use each word in a sentence.

nothing	said
want	what
would	saw

Name ______________________________

High-Frequency Words

Practice

1. Cut out the words.
2. Look for words you know.
3. Ask a partner or teacher about words you do not know.
4. Use each word in a sentence.

says	they
where	you
your	here

Name ______________________

High-Frequency Words

Practice

1. Cut out the words.
2. Look for words you know.
3. Ask a partner or teacher about words you do not know.
4. Use each word in a sentence.

are	one
soft	two
again	does

Name ______________________________

High-Frequency Words

Practice

1. Cut out the words.
2. Look for words you know.
3. Ask a partner or teacher about words you do not know.
4. Use each word in a sentence.

move	onto
our	warm
watch	was

Name ____________________

High-Frequency Words

Practice

1. Cut out the words.
2. Look for words you know.
3. Ask a partner or teacher about words you do not know.
4. Use each word in a sentence.

all	around
could	many
more	nearly

Name ____________________________

High-Frequency Words

Practice

1. Cut out the words.
2. Look for words you know.
3. Ask a partner or teacher about words you do not know.
4. Use each word in a sentence.

put	some
there	another
how	now

Name ______________________

High-Frequency Words

Practice

1. Cut out the words.
2. Look for words you know.
3. Ask a partner or teacher about words you do not know.
4. Use each word in a sentence.

coming	oh
their	water
give	doesn't

Name ______________________________

High-Frequency Words

Practice

1. Cut out the words.
2. Look for words you know.
3. Ask a partner or teacher about words you do not know.
4. Use each word in a sentence.

don't	friends
out	tall
walking	through

Name ___________________________

High-Frequency Words

Practice

1. Cut out the words.
2. Look for words you know.
3. Ask a partner or teacher about words you do not know.
4. Use each word in a sentence.

outside	school
something	gone
great	only

Name ______________________

High-Frequency Words

Practice

1. Cut out the words.
2. Look for words you know.
3. Ask a partner or teacher about words you do not know.
4. Use each word in a sentence.

pulled	upon
about	anything
every	without

Name ______________________________

High-Frequency Words

Practice

1. Cut out the words.
2. Look for words you know.
3. Ask a partner or teacher about words you do not know.
4. Use each word in a sentence.

air	bear
building	fruit
wear	wears

Name ______________________

High-Frequency Words

Practice

1. Cut out the words.
2. Look for words you know.
3. Ask a partner or teacher about words you do not know.
4. Use each word in a sentence.

who	care
laugh	laughed
lives	loves

Name ____________________________

High-Frequency Words

Practice

1. Cut out the words.
2. Look for words you know.
3. Ask a partner or teacher about words you do not know.
4. Use each word in a sentence.

should	began
ear	really
today	together

Name ______________________________

High-Frequency Words

Practice

1. Cut out the words.
2. Look for words you know.
3. Ask a partner or teacher about words you do not know.
4. Use each word in a sentence.

eyes	long
practice	prepared
answer	people

Name ______________________________

High-Frequency Words

Practice

1. Cut out the words.
2. Look for words you know.
3. Ask a partner or teacher about words you do not know.
4. Use each word in a sentence.

been	brother
stronger	year
country	clothes

Name ______________________________

High-Frequency Words

Practice

1. Cut out the words.
2. Look for words you know.
3. Ask a partner or teacher about words you do not know.
4. Use each word in a sentence.

enough	government
money	picture
return	someone

Name ____________________

High-Frequency Words

Practice

1. Cut out the words.
2. Look for words you know.
3. Ask a partner or teacher about words you do not know.
4. Use each word in a sentence.

sometimes	word
break	father
friendless	mother

Name ______________________

High-Frequency Words

Practice

1. Cut out the words.
2. Look for words you know.
3. Ask a partner or teacher about words you do not know.
4. Use each word in a sentence.

mountain	once
river	song
whose	discovers

Name ______________________

High-Frequency Words

Practice

1. Cut out the words.
2. Look for words you know.
3. Ask a partner or teacher about words you do not know.
4. Use each word in a sentence.

everyone	special
sure	body
hours	minute

Name ______________________

High-Frequency Words

Practice

1. Cut out the word.
2. Ask a partner or teacher about the word if you do not know it.
3. Use the word in a sentence.

Standard
4

3

Lesson A

Develop Fluency

Reading with **fluency** means reading something the way it should be read aloud.

There are different ways you can build your skills. Start by learning how to read with purpose and understanding.

Read with Purpose and Understanding

When you see a new passage, read it to yourself. As you read, try to figure out what the passage is about. You want to **understand** the passage. To check that you understand it, ask yourself these questions:

- What is the topic?
- What is the passage about?

If you understand the passage, you can figure out the **purpose** of the writing. Authors write to entertain, inform, or persuade their readers. The purpose helps you know how to speak when you read the passage out loud.

- For example, if the purpose is to entertain people with a happy story, you should speak in a cheerful voice.

To help you identify the purpose, ask yourself these questions:

- Why did the author write this?
- How does the purpose affect the way I speak?

Now turn to pages 227 to listen and learn about reading with purpose and understanding. Then turn to page 228 to practice reading with purpose and understanding.

Name ______________________

Read with Purpose and Understanding

Listen and Learn

1. Type in your *Common Core State Standards Literacy eHandbook address* into your browser's address bar.
2. Click on Part 3 Reading: Foundational Skills in the first Table of Contents.
3. Go to 3.2 Fluency in the second Table of Contents.
4. Click on Lesson A Develop Fluency.
5. Click on Read with Purpose and Understanding.
6. Click on Listen and Learn.

Some kinds of wild weather can be dangerous! A tornado is a tube of spinning air. It is like a vacuum cleaner, sucking up anything in its path. Tornadoes move quickly. But most last only a few minutes.

1. What is the selection about?
2. Why do you think the author wrote this?
3. How did the speaker read the selection?
4. Did her voice match the author's purpose?

Name ______________________

Fluency

Choose one of the fluency passages. Read the passage silently to yourself. Then practice reading the passage aloud. When you are ready, read the passage aloud to a partner. Focus on reading with purpose and understanding. Ask yourself these questions:

- What is the topic of the passage?
- What is the purpose of the passage?
- How will the topic and purpose affect the way I read?

Story

Poetry

Nonfiction

Read with Accuracy, Appropriate Rate, Phrasing, and Expression

Reading with fluency is like acting.
A fluent reader reads a selection aloud
as an actor would say it.

Fluent readers read accurately, with a
natural rate and phrasing, and with expression.

Learn about these skills:

- Accuracy
- Rate
- Phrasing
- Expression

3

Accuracy

Accuracy means reading the words correctly. Reading the words accurately can help you understand a passage.

There are strategies you can use to help you read words. One strategy is sounding out the letters to figure out a word.

For example, if you do not know how to say the word *invent*, look at each letter. Ask yourself, "What sound does each letter make?" Then combine the sounds together to read the word.

Rate

Rate is the speed, or pace, at which you speak. Readers need to speak at a natural pace so listeners can understand the reading. Reading too fast or too slow makes it hard to understand what is being read.

To sound natural, readers pause, stop, and change their rate. Readers may speed up or slow down as they speak.

A reader might read these lines quickly:

> Come on! Let's clean up so we can go to the store.

A reader might read these lines more slowly:

> No one wanted to step outside because it was so cold.

3

Phrasing

When you pause or stop, you are using **phrasing**.

Clues, such as end punctuation, tell you when to stop.

Let's try it!

Read these sentences:

- Would you like to have a pony?
- Feeding a pony is an important responsibility.
- The main foods that a pony eats are hay and grain.
- Ponies also like carrots, apples, and lumps of sugar for snacks.

Did you stop at the end of each sentence?

Did you pause at the commas?

Remember to stop after a period, a question mark, or an exclamation point.

Expression

When you read with **expression**, you show feelings with your voice.

To read with expression, think about how the passage makes you feel. Does it make you feel happy, angry, scared, sad, or excited?

As you speak, change your voice to show those feelings.

Let's try it!

What voice would you use to read the sentence below?

> I was worried about what my father would say after he found out that I lost his baseball.

You can use a scared voice.

What voice would you use to read this sentence?

> I couldn't wait until Friday, which was when we were going to the museum.

You can use a cheerful voice.

Now turn to pages 234–235 to listen and learn about reading with accuracy, natural rate and phrasing, and expression.

3

Name ____________________________

Read with Accuracy, Appropriate Rate, Phrasing, and Expression

Listen and Learn

1. Type in your *Common Core State Standards Literacy eHandbook address* into your browser's address bar.
2. Click on Part 3 Reading: Foundational Skills in the first Table of Contents.
3. Go to 3.2 Fluency in the second Table of Contents.
4. Click on Lesson A Develop Fluency.
5. Click on Read with Accurace, Appropriate Rate, and Expression.
6. Click on Listen and Learn.

Some kinds of wild weather can be dangerous! A tornado is a tube of spinning air. It is like a vacuum cleaner, sucking up anything in its path. Tornadoes move quickly. But most last only a few minutes.

1. Did the speaker correctly read all of the words?
2. Did the speaker speed up or slow down when she said, "Then it may move slowly toward land"?
3. When does the speaker pause or stop?
4. How does the passage make you feel?

Name ____________________________

Fluency

Choose one of the fluency passages. Read the passage to yourself. Then read it aloud. Try to read the words correctly. Think about when you should stop, pause, speed up, or slow down. Think about how you can show expression. When you are ready, read the passage aloud to a partner.

Story

The Poster Contest on page 241
The Mouse and the Lion on page 242

Poetry

Real-Life Heroes on page 243
Who Has Seen the Wind? on page 244

Nonfiction

My Tree on page 245
The Blue Whale on page 246

Use Self-Monitoring Strategies

As you read, you may see a word that you do not know. Use these strategies to help you.

- Reread the sentence.
- Read On to see if the author explains the word later.
- Slow Down to see if you missed any clues about the word
- Sound Out the word.

Reread

As you read a sentence, ask yourself, "Do the words make sense?"

If the answer is no, reread the sentence to figure out the right word.

Imagine that Leon read this sentence aloud:

> Water comes to Earth as pain and snow.

The word *pain* does not make sense in the sentence. Leon should have said the word *rain* instead. When he thought about the sentence, he knew he should say this:

> Water comes to Earth as rain and snow.

Read On

Sometimes writers use context clues to explain words in a passage. Context clues are words and phrases that help you understand a word. If you do not know one of the words, read on to see if the writer explains it.

Drew read the following sentence:

> You are a citizen.

Ami did not know the word *citizen*. So Ami read on and saw this sentence:

> A citizen is someone who is a member of a country or of a community.

Then Ami knew what a citizen was.

If you're still unsure of how to say a word, you can use a dictionary or ask for help.

3

Slow Down

If you read too quickly, you might miss some important words. Slow down so that you can read every word.

Carmen was reading this story:

> This morning Milo was unhappy at breakfast. The old toaster sent smoke all over the kitchen. So he had to eat oatmeal with raisins. Raisins are his least favorite food.

Carmen was confused. She didn't understand why Milo was unhappy. She thought Milo liked raisins because they were his favorite food.

Carmen was reading too fast. She missed the word *least* in the last sentence. When Carmen slowed down and read every word, she understood that Milo does not like raisins.

Sound Out

If you do not know how to say a word,
say the sounds that the letters in the word make.

Try it!

Say the sounds that the letters make
in the word *garden*.

Now combine the sounds to say the word.

3

Name ____________________________

Fluency

Choose one of the fluency passages.
Read the passage silently to yourself.
Then read the passage aloud to a partner.
Try these strategies for words you don't know:

- Reread
- Read on
- Slow down
- Say the sounds of each letter

Story

Poetry

Nonfiction

Name ______________________

The Poster Contest

Our teacher told us our school was having an Earth Day poster contest. Wow, I thought. This could be fun and good for the community! I started drawing some sketches. I didn't like my first one, but after a few more tries, I was happy with my picture. I made a bigger copy of it with bright colors, and outlined my letters in black marker.

Our teacher said the judges would choose a winner the next day. I was so excited that I wanted to shout. Then all of a sudden, I was afraid. What if I did not win? That night I could not sleep.

The next day finally came. I tried to sit quietly at my desk. The principal came in. She said, "The winner of the Earth Day poster contest is..." and then she pointed at me. Me? Wow, I won!

Name ________________________

The Mouse and the Lion

Once, a little mouse was running through the forest. He ran right onto a sleeping lion's back. The lion woke up with a roar.

"You ruined my nap!" the lion growled. "I'll have to eat you." The lion grabbed the little mouse.

"Please don't eat me," the mouse squeaked. "Some day I will return your kindness." The lion laughed so hard that the little mouse fell out of his paw.

A week later, the lion walked into a hunter's trap!

The little mouse heard the lion roaring. He ran onto the lion's back and began to chew the ropes. "Thank you, little mouse," the lion said. "I've learned that little friends can be great friends."

Name ___________________________

Real-Life Heroes

Heroes in movies can fly through
the sky and pick up a car without
blinking an eye.

Real heroes are strong—in ways
they can show, but also in ways
that some never know.

A true hero might say, "That is not right."
She'd point out unfairness and
bring it to light.

A hero in real life might put her
foot down to stand up for friends,
herself and her town.

A hero in real life might walk
with someone who's scared
of a bully. That's really no fun.
Heroes in legends fight monsters
and win. Heroes in real life fight
struggles within.

Heroes are strong—in ways they
can show, but also in ways that
some never know.

Name ______________________________

Who Has Seen the Wind?
by Christina Rossetti

Who has seen the wind?
Neither I nor you;
But when the leaves hang trembling
The wind is passing through.

Who has seen the wind?
Neither you nor I;
But when the trees bow down their heads
The wind is passing by.

Rossetti, Christina. "Who Has Seen the Wind?"
Sing-Song A Nursery Rhyme Book. 1893.

Name ______________________

My Tree

We have a huge, old tree in
our backyard.

In the spring and summer,
it is covered in bushy clumps
of sweet-smelling green leaves.
I like to lean against its rough,
brown trunk and sit in the cool shade.

In the fall, the leaves turn a lovely
tone of yellow. They glitter like gold
in the sunlight and rustle in the wind.

In winter, the tree is bare. I can see
the big branches twist high up into
the blue sky.

I love my tree because it is
beautiful all year round.

Name ______________________________

The Blue Whale

What is the world's largest mammal? The blue whale takes the prize. Everything about the blue whale is huge. Its tongue is so big that fifty people could stand on it. A blue whale's heart can weigh as much as a car.

Scientists think that the blue whale is the largest animal that has ever lived. The longest blue whale ever measured was 110 feet long. The heaviest weighed almost 200 tons. Of course, this is just a close guess. Scientists have weighed only parts of a dead blue whale to judge its weight.

Even though the blue whale is the largest mammal, it still has some predators. Sometimes sharks and killer whales attack blue whales. But people also used to hunt blue whales. The blue whales are now an endangered species.

Part 4
WRITING
4.1 Text Types and Purposes

Standard
1

4

Lesson A

Write Opinions

You can write to share an opinion. An **opinion** is how you feel about something. In this lesson you will learn how to share your opinion about a topic and a book.

Write Opinions About a Topic

Do you like homework? What is your favorite TV show? Your answers to these questions are your **opinions**. An opinion tells how you feel about a topic.

Writers often share their opinion about a topic by writing about it. They try to convince readers to agree with their opinion.

Features of Opinion Pieces

Good opinion pieces

- **introduce the topic** and **tell an opinion**.
- **give reasons** for the opinion.
- use **linking words** such as *because* and *also*.
- retell the writer's opinion at the **end**.

Now look at this example.

Opinion about a Topic: Model

Look at the model. Find the answers to these questions.

1. Which sentence tells the **topic**? What **opinion** does the writer have about the topic?
2. Which sentences give **reasons**?
3. What **linking words** does the writer use?
4. How does the writer **end** the paragraph?

Getting a Dog

Our family should get a dog. I will offer some of my allowance to help buy one. It won't be a lot of work because I will take care of it. I will feed it every day. On Saturdays I will take it for a walk. Also, it will help guard our house and keep us safe. I think a dog would be a great pet for our family.

Did you find the answers to the questions in the text? Here they are below.

1. Which sentence tells the **topic**? What **opinion** does the writer have about the topic?
   - Our family should get a dog.
2. Which sentences give **reasons**?
   - I will offer some of my allowance to help buy one.
   - It won't be a lot of work because I will take care of it.
   - I will feed it every day.
   - On Saturdays I will take it for a walk.
   - Also, it will help guard our house and keep us safe.
3. What **linking words** does the writer use?
   - because
   - Also
4. How does the writer **end** the paragraph?
   - I think a dog would be a great pet for our family.

Writing Process

Now you are ready to write your own opinion about a topic. Follow the steps of the writing process.

- Prewrite
- Draft
- Revise
- Edit
- Publish and Present

Prewrite

An **opinion** is how you feel about a topic. Writers choose a **topic** they feel strongly about. They list reasons for their opinion. **Reasons** tell why you have the opinion you do. Good reasons convince readers to agree with you.

Study the Model

Look at this model. It tells the topic, opinion, and reasons.

Topic: the library

My opinion: It's a great place to go.

My reasons are:
1. Lots to do
2. Librarian is nice
3. Hear stories
4. Play computer games
5. Pick out books

TECHNOLOGY TIP!
Does your class have an online message board? You can use it to help you choose a topic. You can post your ideas. Classmates can reply to your post.

Turn to page 252 to plan your writing.

4

Name ______________________

Plan Your Writing

Practice

What opinion do you want to share? Finish the sentences.

1. My topic is ______________________
2. My opinion is

____

____

3. My reasons are

____

____

____

____

Draft

The next step is to write sentences. Put sentences in an order that makes sense.

- First, tell the **topic** and give your **opinion**.
- Next, give **reasons** why readers should agree with your opinion. Use **linking words** to connect your opinion and your reasons.
- Last, write the **ending**. The ending gives readers something to think about.

Study the Model

Look at the model. Find the writer's opinion, the reasons, and the ending.

> I think kids should visit the library more often. There is so much to do. Kids can listen to stories. They can check out books. Also, there are a lot of fun games to play on the library's computers. The librarian is very nice and she knows a lot. She is helpful. She helps kids pick out good books. The library is a good place to go.

4

Did you find them? Here they are.

The **opinion** is:

- I think kids should visit the library more often.

The **reasons** are:

- There is so much to do.
- Kids can listen to stories.
- They can check out books.
- Also, there are a lot of fun games to play on the library's computers.
- The librarian is very nice and she knows a lot.
- She is helpful.
- She helps kids pick out good books.

The **ending** is:

- The library is a good place to go.

TECHNOLOGY TIP!
Use a computer to type your sentences. Save your file. Be sure to give the file a clear name so you can easily find your file later.

Practice

Use your ideas from the **Plan Your Writing** worksheet to write sentences.

1. First, tell your topic and your opinion.
2. Then, give reasons. Use linking words to connect your ideas.
3. Last, write an ending.

4

Revise

Revising offers a chance to make your ideas clearer. Revising also makes writing more interesting. To revise, writers may

- add details or linking words.
- delete ideas that don't tell about the topic.
- change boring words to more interesting words.
- move ideas around so they are clear.

Study the Model

Look at the model. What details did the writer add? What repeated word did she replace?

Kids should visit the library more often. There is so much to do. Kids can listen to stories. They can check out interesting books and movies. Also, there are a lot of fun games to play on the library's computers. The librarian is very nice and she knows a lot. ~~She is helpful.~~ She helps kids pick out good books. The library is a great ~~good~~ place to go.

TECHNOLOGY TIP!

It is easy to add words with a computer. Use the mouse to place the cursor where you want to add a word. Click once, and then type the word.

CHECKLIST: REVISING

- ☐ Is my topic and opinion clear?
- ☐ Did I give good reasons?
- ☐ Are my ideas in an order that makes sense?
- ☐ Did I use linking words to connect my opinion and reasons?
- ☐ Do I have a good ending?

Practice

1. Reread your sentences. Use the Revising Checklist to make changes.
2. Give your draft to a partner.
3. Use the peer review worksheet on page 259 to give your partner feedback.

Name ______________________________

Peer Review

Practice

Read your partner's draft. Then answer the questions.

Share your answers with your partner.

1. What I liked most was

____

____

2. One question I have for the author is

____

____

3. Here's one idea the author could use:

____

____

Edit

Writers reread their drafts to fix any mistakes.

They make sure that

- sentences and names begin with capital letters.
- sentences end with a period, question mark, or exclamation point.
- all words are spelled correctly.
- all sentences are complete.

Writers use these marks to correct errors on their drafts.

PROOFREADING MARKS

- # new paragraph
- ^ add
- take out
- ≡ Make a capital letter.
- / Make a small letter.
- (sp) Check the spelling.
- ⊙ Add a period.

Study the Model

Look at this model. What errors did the writer fix?

> Kids should visit the library more. There is so much to do. Kids can (sp) ~~lissen~~ listen to stories. They can check out interesting books and movies. Also, there are a lot of fun games to play on the library's computers. The librarian is very nice and she (sp) ~~knose~~ knows a lot. she helps kids pick out good books. The library is a great place to go.

Practice

1. Reread your draft. Fix any mistakes. Check for one type of mistake at a time.
2. Use proofreading marks to correct errors.

Publish and Present

Writers publish their writing to share it with others. They make a neat final copy. To publish, writers

- make sure there are no errors.
- write each word neatly.
- put space between each word and between each sentence.

TECHNOLOGY TIP!

Use technology to share your writing.

- Post your writing on a class Web site.
- E-mail it to your teacher or classmates.
- Show it on an electronic white board.
- Make an audio recording. Save it as an audio file. Then others can listen to it on an mp3 player.

CHECKLIST: BEFORE YOU PUBLISH

- ☐ Did I share my opinion?
- ☐ Did I give good reasons?
- ☐ Did I put my ideas in order?
- ☐ Did I write an ending?
- ☐ Did I fix all mistakes?

Practice

1. Give your draft one more look.
2. Write or type a neat final copy.
3. Add drawings or photos.
4. Share your writing with others.

Use this rubric to evaluate your writing.

Writing Rubric: Opinion Pieces

	Goals	Yes	Need to Fix
Organization	I tell the topic and my opinion at the beginning. I wrote an ending.	☐	☐
Ideas	I give good reasons for my opinion.	☐	☐
Voice	It sounds like me when I read it aloud.	☐	☐
Word Choice	I use clear words to explain my opinion.	☐	☐
Sentence Fluency	I connect ideas with linking words. I use different kinds of sentences.	☐	☐
Conventions	I use correct spelling and punctuation.	☐	☐

Write Opinions about a Book

A book review shares a writer's opinion about a book. It gives reasons why the writer liked or didn't like the book. Book reviews help readers decide what to read.

Features of Book Reviews

Good book reviews

- **name** the book and the author and **tell** what the book is about.
- **tell an opinion** about the book.
- **give reasons** for the opinion.
- use **linking words** such as *because* and *also.*
- **end** by retelling the writer's opinion.

Look at this example of a book review.

Opinion about a Book: Student Model

Look at the model. Find the answers to these questions.

1. What **book** is the topic of this review?
2. Which sentences tell **what the book is about**?
3. What **opinion** does the writer have? What **reasons** does the writer give?
4. What linking words does the writer use?
5. How does the writer **end** the paragraph?

César E. Chávez: Equal Rights Leader

César E. Chávez: Equal Rights Leader by Don McCleese is an interesting book that tells about César Chávez's life. César was born in Mexico. He believed that all workers should be treated fairly. César was the leader of the United Farm Workers. He went on hunger strikes twice. California celebrates César E. Chávez day every year on his birthday. He died in April 1993.

I really liked this book because it teaches about Chávez's life and how hard he worked to help others. It also shows that a person can do something great in his or her life. I wish I could have met him.

Did you find the answers to the questions in the text? Here they are.

1. What **book** is the topic of this review?

   César E. Chávez: Equal Rights Leader by Don McCleese is an interesting book that tells about César Chávez's life.

2. Which sentences tell **what the book is about**?

   César was born in Mexico. He believed that all workers should be treated fairly. César was the leader of the United Farm Workers. He went on hunger strikes twice. California celebrates César E. Chávez day every year on his birthday. He died in April 1993.

3. What **opinion** does the writer have? What **reasons** does the writer give?

   I really liked this book because it teaches about Chávez's life and how hard he worked to help others. It also shows that a person can do something great in his or her life.

4. What linking words does the writer use?

   because

   also

5. How does the writer **end** the paragraph?

   I wish I could have met him.

4

Writing Process

Now you are ready to write your own opinion about a book. Follow the steps of the writing process.

- Prewrite
- Draft
- Revise
- Edit
- Publish and Present

Prewrite

To begin a book review, choose a **book** you feel strongly about. Tell **what the book is about**. Give reasons for your opinion. **Reasons** tell why you have the opinion you do. Reasons may be facts or opinions. Good reasons convince readers to agree with you.

Study the Model

Look at this model. The writer planned the parts of the book review.

Book: *Corduroy* by Don Freeman

What it's about:

1. Corduroy lives in the store.
2. Lisa wants to buy Corduroy.
3. Lisa comes back and takes him home.

My opinion: I like this book.

Reasons:

1. It's fun to read.
2. It makes me feel good.

TECHNOLOGY TIP!

Does your school or class have an online message board? A message board can help you choose an interesting topic. You can post your ideas. Classmates can reply to your post.

Turn to page 272 to plan your writing.

4

Name ______________________________

Plan Your Writing

What book do you want to write about?
Finish the sentences.

1. My book is

____

2. The book is about

____

____

____

3. My opinion is

____

4. My reasons are

____

____

____

____

Draft

The next step is to write sentences. Writers put their ideas in order.

- First, writers tell the name of the book, the author, and **what the book was about.**
- Then, they give their **opinion** about the book and **reasons** why they feel that way.
- They use **linking words** to connect their opinion and reasons.
- Last, they write an **ending**. They often tell who they think would enjoy the book.

4

Study the Model

Look at the model. Find the writer's opinion, reasons, and ending.

> *Corduroy*, by Don Freeman, is about a toy bearthat lives in a store. At the beginning of the story, he wants someone to buy him and take him home. Lisa wants to buy him, but her mom won't let her. Finally, Lisa comes back and takes him home.
>
> I think this is a great book. It was fun to read, and the characters were interesting. The end made me feel warm and good. Anyone who has ever loved a stuffed animal will like reading this book.

The **opinion** is:

I think this is a great book.

The **reasons** are:

It was fun to read, and the characters were interesting. The end made me feel warm and good.

The **ending** is:

Anyone who has ever loved a stuffed animal will like reading this book.

TECHNOLOGY TIP!
Use a computer to type your sentences. Be sure to save your file. Give the file a clear name so you can find your file later.

Practice

Use your ideas from the **Plan Your Writing** worksheet. Write sentences.

1. Tell the name of the book.
2. Tell what the book is about.
3. Tell your opinion. Give reasons.
4. Write an ending.

4

Revise

Revising makes writing clearer and more interesting. To revise, writers may

- add details and linking words.
- delete words that don't tell about the topic.
- change boring words into more interesting words.
- move ideas around to make them clearer.

Study the Model

Look at the model. What details did the writer add?

Which idea didn't tell about the topic?

Corduroy, by Don Freeman, is about a toy bear that lives in a store. At the beginning of the story, he wants someone to buy him and take him home. Lisa wants to buy him, but her mom won't let her. ^She says it's because she doesn't have the money and he is missing a button.^ Finally, Lisa comes back and takes him home.

I think this is a ~~great~~ ^heart-warming^ book. It was fun to read, and the characters were interesting. ^Also^ The end made me feel warm and good. ^You don't have to be perfect to be loved.^ Anyone who has ever loved a stuffed animal will like reading this book.

4

TECHNOLOGY TIP!

It is easy to add details to your draft on a computer. Use the mouse. Move the cursor to the place where you want to add a word or sentence. Click once. Then type.

CHECKLIST: REVISING

- ☐ Is my opinion clear?
- ☐ Are my ideas in an order that makes sense?
- ☐ Do I have enough reasons?
- ☐ Do I connect my opinion and reasons with linking words?
- ☐ Do all my ideas tell about my topic?

Practice

1. Reread your sentences. Use the checklist to make changes.
2. Next, give your draft to a partner.
3. Use the peer review worksheet on page 279 to give your partner feedback.

Name ______________________

Peer Review

Practice

Read your partner's draft. Then answer the questions.

Share your answers with your partner.

1. What I liked most was

____

____

2. One question I have for the author is

____

____

3. Here's one idea the author could use:

____

____

Edit

Writers reread their drafts to fix mistakes.

They make sure that

- sentences and names begin with capital letters.
- sentences end with a period, question mark, or exclamation point.
- all words are spelled correctly.
- all sentences are complete.

Writers use these marks to correct errors.

PROOFREADING MARKS

- ¶ new paragraph
- ^ add
- take out
- ≡ Make a capital letter.
- / Make a small letter.
- (sp) Check the spelling.
- ⊙ Add a period.

Study the Model

Look at this model. What errors did the writer correct?

Corduroy, by Don Freeman, is about a toy bear that lives in a store. At the beginning of the story, he wants someone to buy him and take him home. Lisa wants to buy him, but her mom won't let her. She says it's because she doesn't have the money and he is missing a button. Finally, Lisa comes back and takes him home.

I think this is a heart-warming book. It was fun to read, and the ~~caracters~~ characters were interesting. Also, the end made me feel warm and good. You don't have to be perfect to be loved. Anyone who has ever loved a stuffed animal will like reading this book.

Practice

1. Reread your draft. Fix any mistakes. Check for one type of mistake at a time.
2. Use proofreading marks to correct mistakes.

4

Publish and Present

Writers publish their writing to share it with others. They make a neat final copy. To publish, writers

- make sure there are no errors.
- write each word neatly.
- put space between each word and between each sentence.

TECHNOLOGY TIP!

Use technology to share your writing.

- Post your writing on a class Web site.
- E-mail your writing to your teacher or classmates.
- Show your writing on an electronic whiteboard.
- Make an audio recording. Save it as an audio file. Then, others can listen to it on an mp3 player.

CHECKLIST: BEFORE YOU PUBLISH

☐ Did I share my opinion?

☐ Did I give convincing reasons?

☐ Did I put my ideas in order?

☐ Did I use linking words to connect my ideas?

☐ Did I write a good ending sentence?

☐ Did I fix any mistakes?

Practice

1. Give your draft one more look.
2. Type or write a neat final copy.
3. Add drawings or photographs, if you wish.
4. Share your writing with others.

After you publish, use this rubric to evaluate your writing.

Writing Rubric: Opinion Pieces

	Goals	Yes	Need to Fix
Organization	I tell the name of the book and the author. I have a summary and give my opinion. I wrote an ending.	☐	☐
Ideas	I give details about the book. I give reasons for my opinion.	☐	☐
Voice	It sounds like me when I read it aloud.	☐	☐
Word Choice	I use describing words.	☐	☐
Sentence Fluency	I use different kinds of sentences.	☐	☐
Conventions	I use correct spelling and punctuation.	☐	☐

Lesson B

Write To Inform and Explain

You can write to share facts about a topic. You can write to explain how to do something or tell how something works. In this lesson you will learn how to inform and explain with writing.

Report

Do you know facts about a topic? You can write a report to tell others what you know. A report tells information about a topic.

Features of Reports

Good reports

- introduce the **topic**.
- use **facts and definitions** to tell about the topic.
- have a **conclusion**, or ending.

Report: Student Model

Look at the model. Find the answers to these questions.

1. Which sentence tells the **topic**?
2. Which sentences give **facts and definitions**?
3. How does the writer **end** the paragraph?

Why It Snows

Have you ever wondered why it snows? It all begins with the sun! The sun heats up water from lakes and rivers. The warm water changes to a gas. It is called water vapor. Water vapor rises up into the sky. It cools off and turns back into water. That is what a cloud is. When the water gets heavy enough, it falls back to Earth. When the air is very cold, the falling water freezes. It clumps together into snow flakes. It's snowing!

4

Did you find the answers to the questions in the text? Here they are.

1. Which sentence tells the **topic**?
   - Have you ever wondered why it snows?
2. Which sentences give **facts and definitions**?
   - It all begins with the sun!
   - The sun heats up water from lakes and rivers.
   - The warm water changes to a gas.
   - It is called water vapor. Water vapor rises up into the sky.
   - It cools off and turns back into water.
   - That is what a cloud is.
   - When the water gets heavy enough, it falls back to Earth.
   - When the air is very cold, the falling water freezes.
   - It clumps together into snow flakes.
3. How does the writer **end** the paragraph?
   - It's snowing!

Writing Process

Now you are ready to write your own opinion about a topic. Follow the steps of the writing process.

- Prewrite
- Draft
- Revise
- Edit
- Publish and Present

Prewrite

A **report** tells about a topic by giving facts and definitions. Sometimes writers choose a **topic** they would like to learn about. Sometimes they choose a topic they would like to tell others about. Then they gather **facts** and **definitions**.

Writers use facts they already know. They may also look for more facts. They may use books, Web sites, or magazines to learn more.

4

Study the Model

This student's topic is hibernation. She used an idea web to gather facts and definitions about hibernation.

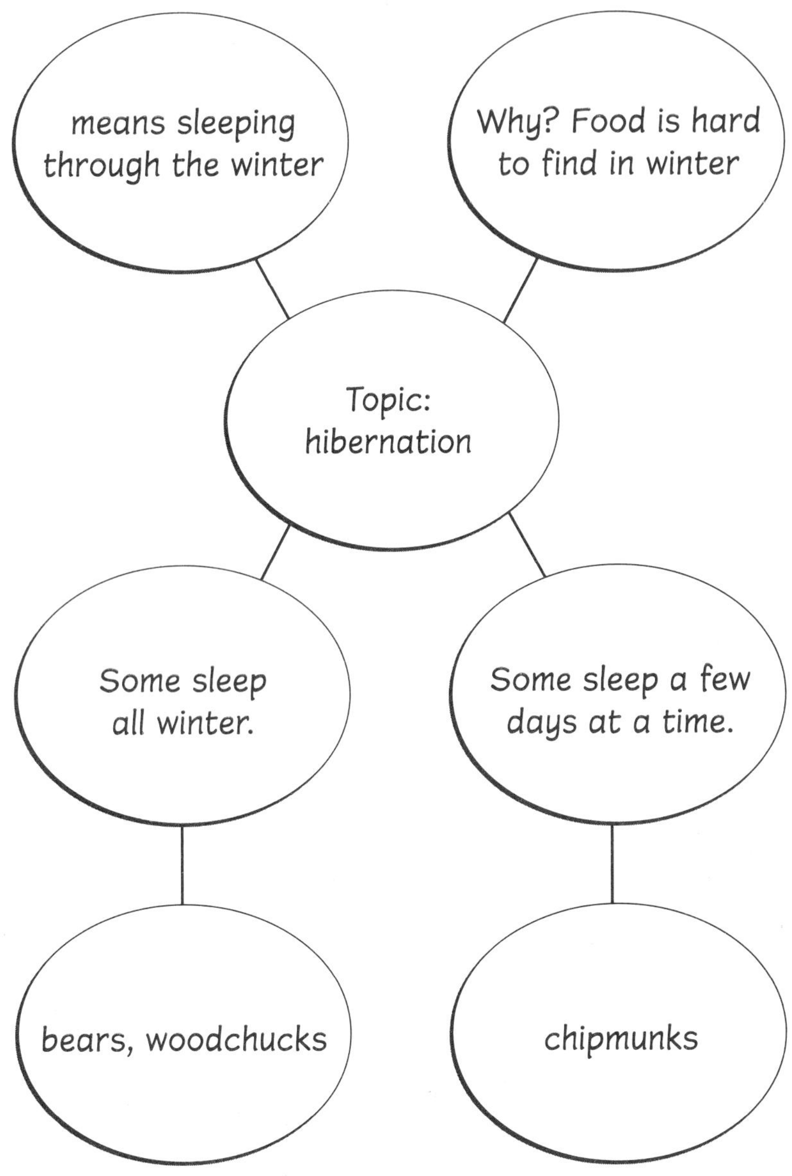

TECHNOLOGY TIP!
You can use an online encyclopedia. It has facts and definitions about many topics. To find information, type your topic into the search box.

Now turn to page 290 to plan your own report.

4

Name ______________________________

Plan Your Writing

Practice

Write your topic in the middle. Write facts and definitions in the outer circles.

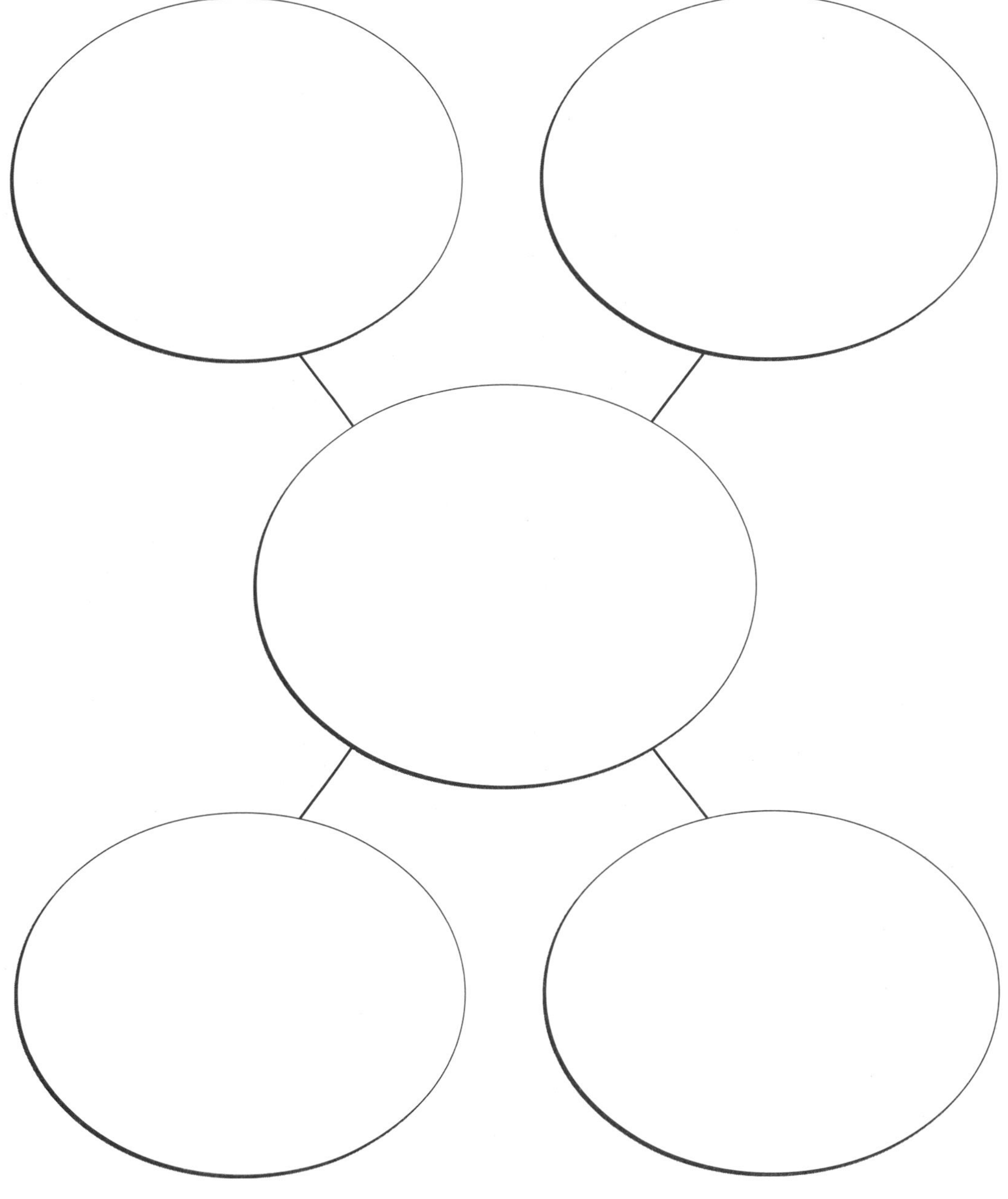

Draft

The next step is to write your first draft. Writers put their ideas in an order that makes sense.

- First, they tell the **topic**.
- Next, they give **facts and definitions** that tell about the topic.
- Last, they write the **conclusion**, or ending. The ending gives readers something to think about.

Study the Model

Look at the student model. Find the topic, facts and definitions, and the ending.

When it gets cold, some animals hibernate to stay alive. Hibernating means sleeping during the winter. Animals hibernate because it is hard to find food when snow covers the ground. Animals such as bears and woodchucks eat a lot before winter. Then they find a place to sleep that is safe from the cold weather. They stay asleep until spring. If the animals don't eat enough before they hibernate, they might die. Other animals, such as chipmunks, sleep for a few days at a time. They wake up and eat some food they stored. Then they go back to sleep. Winter is hard on animals. Hibernating helps them survive.

Here is the **topic**.

- When it gets cold, some animals hibernate to stay alive.

Here are the **sentences with facts and definitions.**

- Hibernating means sleeping during the winter.
- Animals hibernate because it is hard to find food when snow covers the ground.
- Animals such as bears and woodchucks eat a lot before winter.
- Then they find a place to sleep that is safe from the cold weather.
- They stay asleep until spring.
- If the animals don't eat enough before they hibernate, they might die.
- Other animals, such as chipmunks, sleep for a few days at a time.
- They wake up and eat some food they stored.
- Then they go back to sleep.

Here is the **ending**.

- Winter is hard on animals. Hibernating helps them survive.

TECHNOLOGY TIP!

Use a computer to type your sentences. Save your file. Give the file a clear name so you can easily find your file later.

Practice

Use your ideas from the **Plan Your Writing** worksheet to write your first draft.

1. Write a sentence that introduces your topic.
2. Write sentences that tell facts and definitions that explain your topic.
3. End your draft with a concluding statement.

4

Revise

Revising makes ideas clearer and more interesting. To revise their drafts, writers may

- add details.
- delete ideas that don't tell about the topic.
- change boring words to more interesting words.
- move ideas around so they are clear.

Study the Model

Look at the model. What detail did the writer add? What word did she change?

When it gets cold, some animals hibernate to stay alive. Hibernating means sleeping during the winter. Animals hibernate because it is hard to find food when snow covers the ground. Animals such as bears and woodchucks eat a lot before winter. Then they find a place to sleep that is safe from the ~~cold~~ frigid weather. They stay asleep until it gets warm in the spring. If the animals don't eat enough before they hibernate, they might die. Other animals, such as chipmunks, sleep for a few days at a time. They wake up and eat some food they stored. Then they go back to sleep. Winter is hard on animals. Hibernating helps them survive.

4

TECHNOLOGY TIP!

It is easy to move words around with a computer. Use the mouse. Highlight the word. Click and drag it to a new place.

CHECKLIST: REVISING

☐ Is my topic clear?

☐ Are my ideas in an order that makes sense?

☐ Did I include facts and definitions?

☐ Do I have a good ending?

Practice

1. Reread your sentences. Use the Revising Checklist to make changes.
2. Give your draft to a partner.
3. Use the peer review worksheet on page 297 to give your partner feedback.

Name ______________________

Peer Review

Practice

Read your partner's draft. Then answer the questions.

Share your answers with your partner.

1. What I liked most was

____

____

2. One question I have for the author is

____

____

3. Here's one idea the author could use:

____

____

Edit

Writers reread their drafts to fix any mistakes. They make sure that

- sentences and names begin with capital letters.
- sentences end with a period, question mark, or exclamation point.
- all words are spelled correctly.
- all sentences are complete.

Writers use these marks to correct errors on their drafts.

PROOFREADING MARKS

- ¶ new paragraph
- ^ add
- take out
- ≡ Make a capital letter.
- / Make a small letter.
- (SP) Check the spelling.
- ⊙ Add a period.

Study the Model

Look at this model. What errors did the writer fix?

When it gets cold, some animals hibernate to stay alive. Hibernating means sleeping during the Winter. Animals hibernate because it is hard to find food when snow covers the ground. Animals such as bears and woodchucks eat a lot before winter. Then they find a place to sleep that is safe from the frigid weather. They stay asleep until it gets warm in the Spring. If the animals don't eat enough ~~enuff~~ (SP) before they hibernate, they might die. Other animals, such as chipmunks, sleep for a few days at a time. They wake up and eat some food they stored. Then they go back to sleep. Winter is hard on animals. Hibernating helps them survive.

Practice

1. Reread your draft. Fix any mistakes. Check for one type of mistake at a time.
2. Use proofreading marks to correct errors.

4

Publish and Present

Writers publish their writing to share it with others. They make a neat final copy. To publish, writers

- make sure there are no errors.
- write each word neatly.
- put space between each word and between each sentence.

TECHNOLOGY TIP!

Use technology to share your writing.

- Post your writing on a class Web site.
- E-mail it to your teacher or classmates.
- Show it on an electronic white board.
- Make an audio recording. Save it as an audio file. Then others can listen to it on an mp3 player.

CHECKLIST: BEFORE YOU PUBLISH

☐ Did I introduce my topic?

☐ Did I use facts and definitions to explain my topic?

☐ Did I put my ideas in order?

☐ Did I write an ending?

☐ Did I fix all mistakes?

Practice

Give your draft one more look.

1. Write or type a neat final copy.
2. Add drawings or photos.
3. Share your writing with others.

Use this rubric to evaluate your writing.

Writing Rubric: Report

	Goals	Yes	Need to Fix
Organization	I tell the topic at the beginning. I use the middle to give facts and definitions. I have an ending.	☐	☐
Ideas	I have an interesting topic. I use interesting facts and clear definitions.	☐	☐
Voice	It sounds like me when I read it aloud.	☐	☐
Word Choice	I use interesting words.	☐	☐
Sentence Fluency	I use different kinds of sentences.	☐	☐
Conventions	I use correct spelling and punctuation.	☐	☐

4

How-to Writing

How do you make a paper airplane? How does an mp3 player work? How-to writing may explain how to do something. It may explain how something works.

Features of How-to Pieces

Good how-to pieces

- have a **topic** that tells how to do or make something.
- list **steps** in order.
- use **facts** and **definitions** to explain the steps.
- have a **concluding** statement, or ending.

How-to Writing: Student Model

Look at the model. Find the answers to these questions.

1. What does the writer tell how to do?
2. What **facts and definitions** does the writer give?
3. What **time-order words** does the writer use?
4. How does the writer **end** the paragraph?

Make a Home for Your Goldfish

Goldfish make great pets. You can make their fish bowl a nice place for them to live. First, use soap and water to wash some pebbles, a plastic castle, and plastic plants. Next, add the pebbles to the fish bowl. Pebbles are the base that will hold the other items in place. They should be about two inches deep. Then, add the plastic castle and plants. These are a good idea because goldfish need someplace to hide. Slowly fill the bowl with water. Finally, place the bowl somewhere quiet. Fish don't like a lot of noise. After you add your fish, watch them enjoy their new home!

4

Did you find the answers to the questions in the text? Here they are.

1. What does the writer tell how to do?
   - Goldfish make great pets. You can make their fish bowl a nice place for them to live.

2. What **facts and definitions** does the writer give?
   - First, use soap and water to wash some pebbles, a plastic castle, and plastic plants. Next, add the pebbles to the fish bowl. Pebbles are the base that will hold the other items in place. They should be about two inches deep. Then, add the plastic castle and plants. These are a good idea because goldfish need someplace to hide. Slowly fill the bowl with water. Finally, place the bowl somewhere quiet. Fish don't like a lot of noise.

3. What **time-order words** does the writer use?
   - First
   - Next
   - Then
   - Finally

4. How does the writer **end** the paragraph?
   - After you add your fish, watch them enjoy their new home!

Writing Process

Now you are ready to write your own how-to piece. Follow the steps of the writing process.

- Prewrite
- Draft
- Revise
- Edit
- Publish and Present

Prewrite

To begin a how-to piece, writers choose a **topic** they would like to explain. Writers often choose to write about something they already know how to do. They choose a topic that will interest their readers.

Next, they list each step. They brainstorm **facts** and **definitions** that explain the process. They put the steps in order.

4

Study the Model

This student will tell how to play a game. She has four steps. They are in order. She used facts and definitions that explain the process.

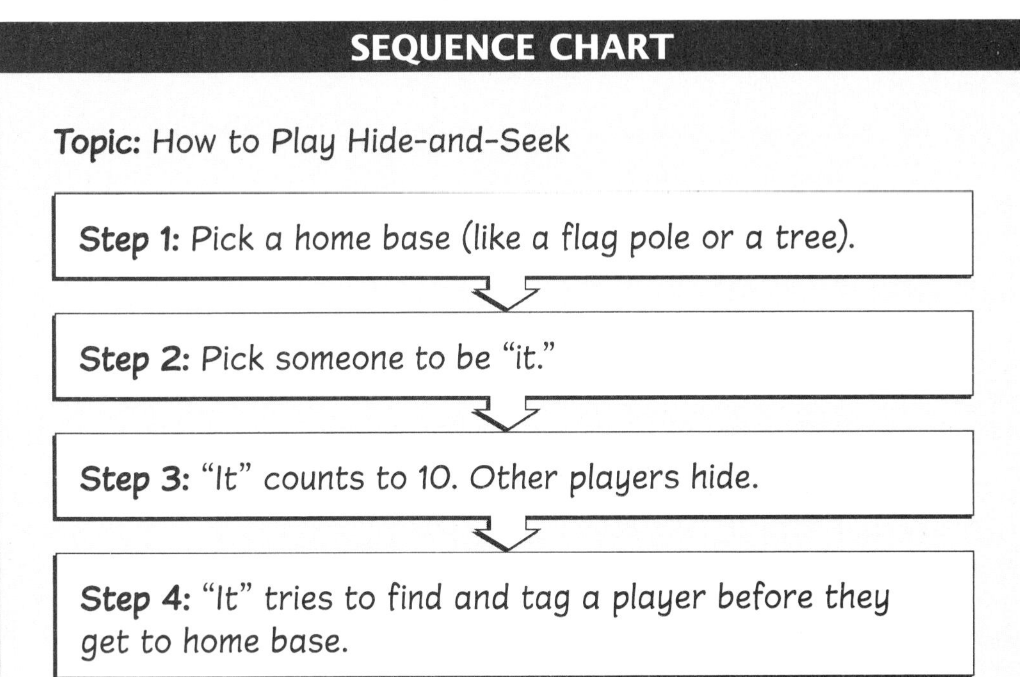

TECHNOLOGY TIP!
Use a computer to type the steps. That way, you can click and drag to put the steps in order.

Turn to page 307 to plan your own how-to writing.

Name ______________________________

Plan Your Writing

Practice

Write your how-to topic. Write the steps in order.

Add facts and details.

My How-to Topic: ____________________

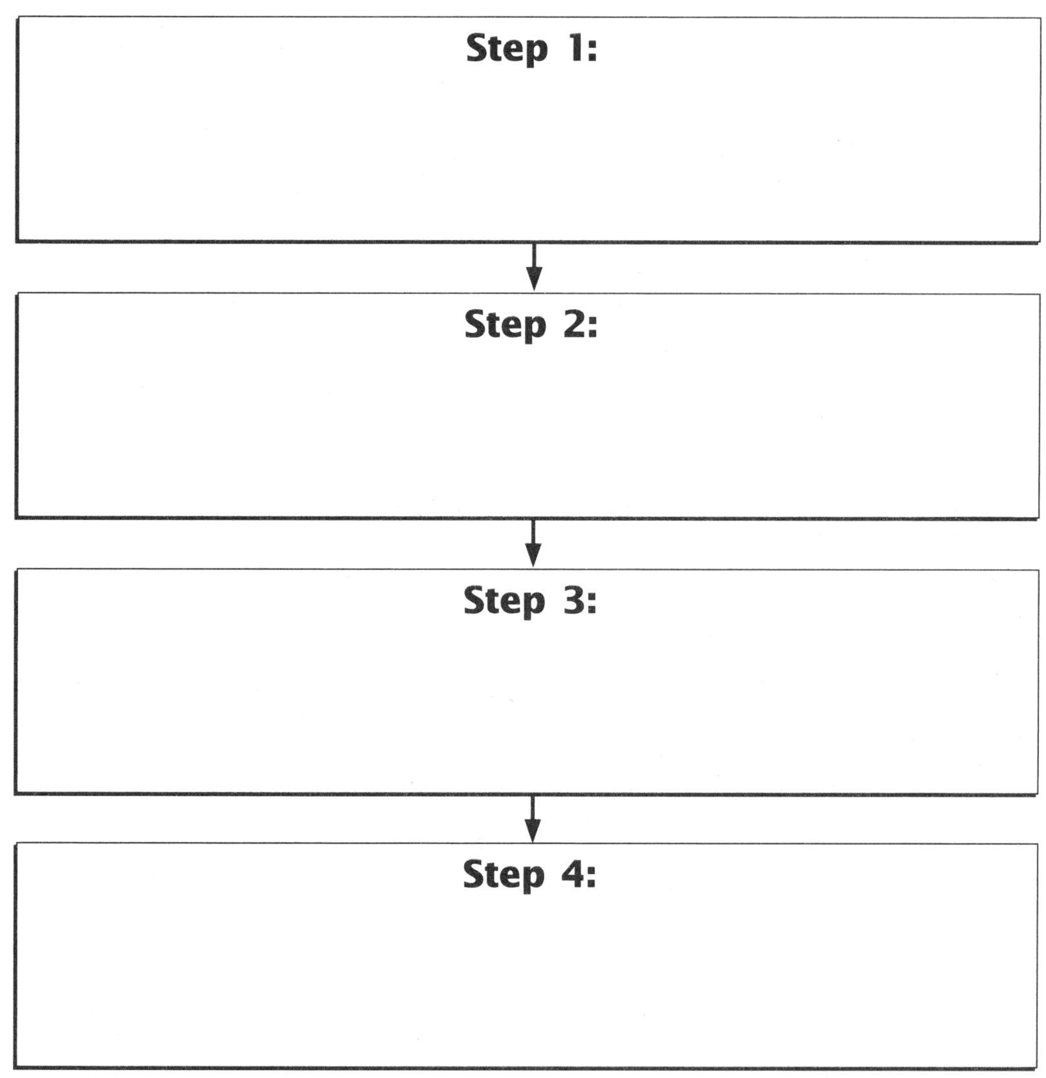

Draft

The next step is to write a first draft. Writers put their ideas in order.

- First, writers introduce the **topic**.
- Next, they tell the **steps** in order. They use words such as *first*, *next*, and *last*.
- They use **facts** and **definitions** to explain the process.
- Last, they write an **ending**.

Study the Model

Look at the model. Find the topic. Look for each step. The words *first, next,* and *after that* help readers follow the order of the steps. Now find the ending.

Hide-and-seek is a fun and easy game to play during recess. All you need is at least four people. First, pick a home base. Home base is where players go to be "safe." Next, pick one player to be "it." That player counts to ten while everyone else runs and hides. After that, "it" tries to find and tag the other players. The other players run for home base without getting tagged by "it." Next time you're at recess, play hide-and-seek. You'll love it!

Here is the **topic**.

- Hide-and-seek is a fun and easy game to play during recess.

Here are the **steps**.

- First, pick a home base. Home base is where players go to be "safe."
- Next, pick one player to be "it." That player counts to ten while everyone else runs and hides.
- After that, "it" tries to find and tag the other players. The other players run for home base without getting tagged by "it."

Here is the **ending**.

- Next time you're at recess, play hide-and-seek. You'll love it!

TECHNOLOGY TIP!
Use a computer to type your draft. Be sure to save your file. Give the file a clear name so you can easily find your file later.

Practice

Use your ideas from the **Plan Your Writing** worksheet. Write sentences.

1. First, write a sentence that tells your topic.
2. Then, write your steps in order. Use facts and definitions to explain the process.
3. Finally, write an ending.

4

Revise

Revising makes writing clearer and more interesting. To revise, writers may

- add details.
- delete words that don't tell about the topic.
- change boring words into more interesting words.
- move ideas around to make them clearer.

Study the Model

Look at the model. What detail did the writer add? Which idea did the writer make clearer?

Hide-and-seek is a fun and easy game to play during recess. All you need is at least four people. First, pick a home base. Home base is where players go to be "safe." ^A tree or flag pole is a good home base.^ Next, pick one player to be "it." That player counts to ten while everyone else runs and hides. After that, "it" tries to find and tag the other players. The other players ^try to^ run for home base without getting tagged by "it." Next time you're at recess, play hide-and-seek. You'll love it!

TECHNOLOGY TIP!

Use technology to get feedback. E-mail your draft to your partner or teacher. They can type comments. Then they can e-mail it back to you.

4

CHECKLIST: REVISING

☐ Is my topic clear?

☐ Are my steps in order?

☐ Did I leave out important steps?

☐ Do I have enough facts? Do I define words readers might not know?

Practice

1. Reread your sentences. Use the Revising checklist to make changes.
2. Give your draft to a partner.
3. Use the peer review worksheet on page 313 to give your partner feedback.

Name ____________________________

Peer Review

Practice

Read your partner's draft. Then answer the questions.

Share your answers with your partner.

1. What I liked most was

____

____

2. One question I have for the author is

____

____

3. Here's one idea the author could use:

____

____

Edit

Writers reread their drafts to fix mistakes.

They make sure that

- sentences and names begin with capital letters.
- sentences end with a period, question mark, or exclamation point.
- all words are spelled correctly.
- all sentences are complete.

Writers use these marks to correct errors.

PROOFREADING MARKS

- # new paragraph
- ^ add
- take out
- ≡ Make a capital letter.
- / Make a small letter.
- (sp) Check the spelling.
- ⊙ Add a period.

Study the Model

Look at this student model. What errors did the writer correct?

Hide-and-seek is a fun and easy game to play during recess. All you need is at least four people. First, pick a home base. Home base is where players go to be "safe." A tree or flag pole is a good home base. Next, pick one player to be "it." That player counts to ten while everyone else runs and hides. After that, "it" tries to find and tag the other players. The other players try to run for home base without getting tagged by "it." Next time you're at recess, play hide-and-seek. You'll love it!

Practice

1. Reread your draft. Fix any mistakes. Check for one type of mistake at a time.
2. Use proofreading marks to correct mistakes.

4

Publish and Present

Writers publish their writing to share it with others. They make a neat final copy. To publish, writers

- make sure there are no errors.
- write each word neatly.
- put space between each word and between each sentence.

TECHNOLOGY TIP!

Use technology to share your writing.

- Post your writing on a class Web site.
- E-mail your writing to your teacher or classmates.
- Show your writing on an electronic whiteboard.
- Make an audio recording. Save it as an audio file. Then, others can listen to it on an mp3 player.

CHECKLIST: BEFORE YOU PUBLISH

☐ Did I introduce my topic?

☐ Did I put the steps in order?

☐ Did I use facts and definitions to explain the process?

☐ Did I write a good concluding section or sentence?

☐ Did I fix any mistakes?

Practice

1. Give your draft one more look.
2. Type or write a neat final copy.
3. Add drawings or photographs, if you wish.
4. Share your writing with others.

Use this rubric to evaluate your writing.

Writing Rubric: How-to Pieces

	Goals	Yes	Need to Fix
Organization	I tell the topic at the beginning. The steps are in order.	☐	☐
Ideas	I clearly explain all the steps. I give facts and definitions to help readers understand the process.	☐	☐
Voice	It sounds like me when I read it aloud.	☐	☐
Word Choice	I use clear words to explain the steps.	☐	☐
Sentence Fluency	I use time-order words to show the order of the steps.	☐	☐
Conventions	I use correct spelling and punctuation.	☐	☐

4

Standard 3

4

Lesson C

Write Narrative Texts

In a personal narrative, writers recount real events that happened to them. Writers make up stories too. In this lesson, you'll learn about writing a personal narrative and a story.

Personal Narrative

What is the funniest thing you have done? What is your favorite memory? You can write about things that happened to you. **Personal narratives** tell real stories about the writer's life. They tell how the writer felt.

Features of Personal Narratives

Good personal narratives

- tell about events that really happened.
- use the words ***I* and *me***.
- use **details** to describe actions, thoughts, and feelings.
- have a **beginning**, **middle**, and **end**.
- use **temporal words** to show what happened first, next, and last.

Personal Narrative: Student Model

Look at the model. Find the answers to these questions.

1. What **temporal words** does the writer use to show the order of events?
2. What **details** does the writer use to describe actions, thoughts, and feelings?
3. How does the writer **feel** at the end?

4

Moving

When I first moved here, I was sad about leaving my friends. I did not want to come out of my room. What if no one liked me?

Then one day there was a loud knock at the door. A boy in a blue bathing suit was standing there. He grinned, and I saw he was missing a tooth. I couldn't help but smile back shyly. "Hey!" he said. "I'm Marcus. You're my neighbor!" Then he asked if I liked to swim. His family had just gotten a pool.

After that day, Marcus and I became friends. He helped me make other friends, too. Moving wasn't so bad after all, thanks to Marcus.

1. What **temporal words** does the writer use to show the order of events?
   - Then one day
   - Then
   - After that day

2. What **details** does the writer use to describe actions, thoughts, and feelings?

When I first moved here, I was sad about leaving my friends. I did not want to come out of my room. What if no one liked me?

Then one day there was a loud knock at the door. A boy in a blue bathing suit was standing there. He grinned, and I saw he was missing a tooth. I couldn't help but smile back shyly. "Hey!" he said. "I'm Marcus. You're my neighbor!" Then he asked if I liked to swim. His family had just gotten a pool.

After that day, Marcus and I became friends. He helped me make other friends, too.

3. How does the writer **feel** at the end?

Moving wasn't so bad after all, thanks to Marcus.

4

Writing Process

Now you are ready to write your own personal narrative. Follow the steps of the writing process.

- Prewrite
- Draft
- Revise
- Edit
- Publish and Present

Prewrite

A **personal narrative** is a story that really happened to you. It tells the events in order. It tells how you felt. It includes many details that help readers understand the actions, thoughts, and feelings of the people in the story.

To begin, writers choose an interesting **topic**. They think about what happened **first, next,** and **last**. They brainstorm **details** that describe what happened and how they felt.

Study the Model

Look at the model.

MY TOPIC: Teaching Max Tricks

Beginning:
problem with my puppy Max

Middle:
- wanted to teach him tricks
- practiced every day
- taught him to shake, fetch, and roll over

End:
He put on a show.
Maybe I'll become a trainer.

TECHNOLOGY TIP!

Use a computer to brainstorm what happened first, next, and last. A computer makes it easy to add ideas. You can change the order, too. Highlight and drag ideas to a new place.

Now turn to page 324 to plan your own personal narrative.

4

Name ______________________________

Plan Your Writing

Practice

Write your topic. Brainstorm what happened first, next, and last. Add details that describe what happened and how you felt.

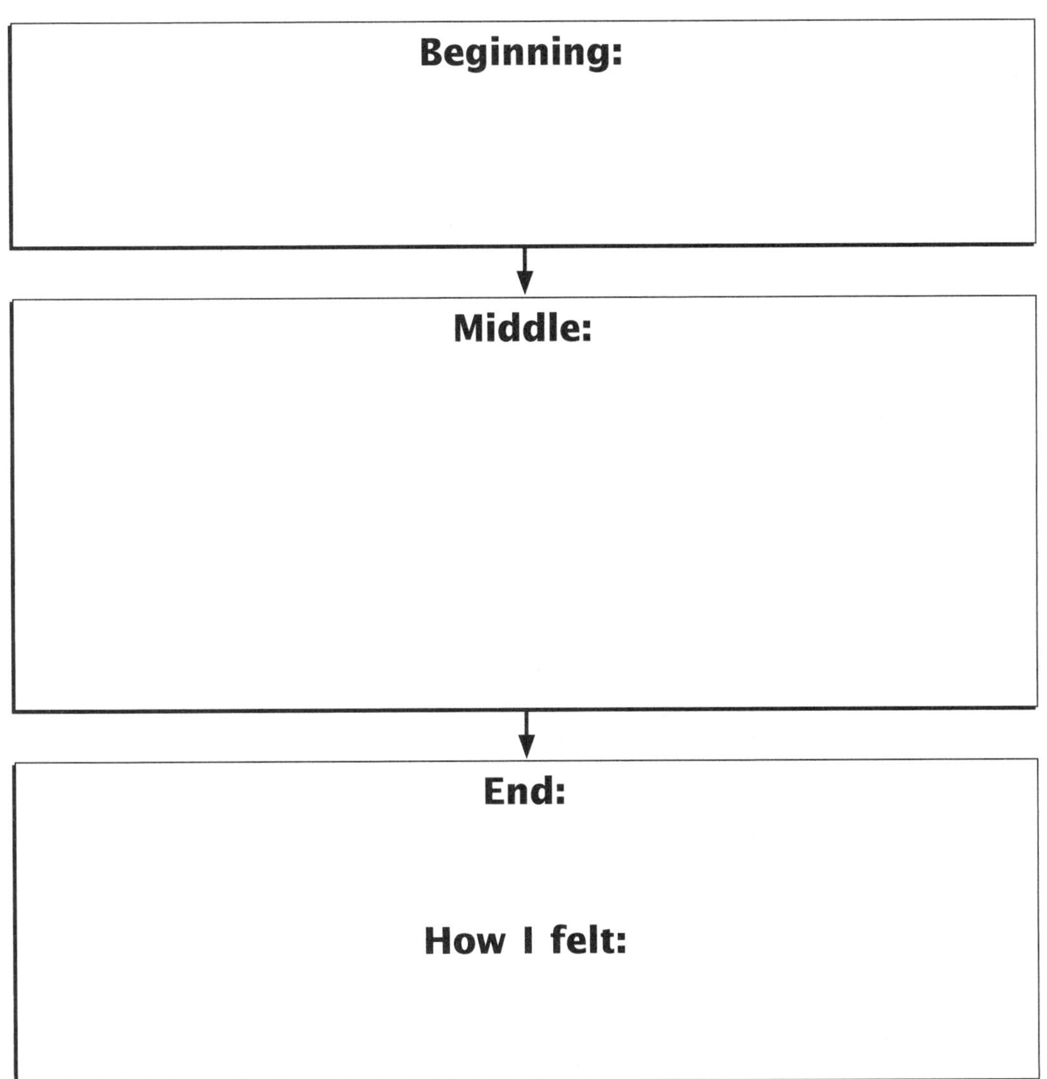

Draft

The next step is to write sentences.

- A good **beginning** makes readers want to find out what happens next.
- The middle tells about the event in **sequence**, or order.
- **Temporal words** help readers understand what happened first, next, and last.
- Good **details** describe what happened and what people thought or felt.
- Finally, the **ending** tells how the writer felt.

TEMPORAL WORDS

You can use these words in your writing:

first
next
then
later
after that
soon
last
finally

4

Study the Model

Look at the model. Find the details, temporal words, and the writer's feelings.

I had a problem with my puppy. Max was cute and cuddly, but he didn't know how to do much. My friend Jesse had a smart dog that could do all kinds of tricks. I wanted Max to do tricks too. I worked with Max every day after school. First, I taught him to shake. Then I taught him to fetch. Next, I taught him to roll over! Finally, I showed Jesse all his tricks. I was so proud. Maybe I will be a dog trainer when I get older.

Here are the **details**.

Max was cute and cuddly, but he didn't know how to do much. My friend Jesse had a smart dog that could do all kinds of tricks. I wanted Max to do tricks too. I worked with Max every day after school. First, I taught him to shake. Then I taught him to fetch. Next, I taught him to roll over! Finally, I showed Jesse all his tricks.

Here are the **temporal words**.

- First
- Then
- Next
- Finally

Here is **how the writer felt**.

- I was so proud. Maybe I will be a dog trainer when I get older.

TECHNOLOGY TIP!
Use a computer to type your sentences. Save your file. Give the file a clear name. A clear name will help you find your file later.

Practice

Use your ideas from the **Plan Your Writing** worksheet to write a first draft.

1. First, write a good beginning.
2. Then, share details in order. Use temporal words.
3. Last, write an ending that tells how you felt.

4

Revise

Revising makes ideas clearer. It makes writing more interesting. To revise, writers may

- add details to elaborate on the events.
- delete ideas that don't tell about the topic.
- change boring words to more interesting words.
- move ideas around so they are clear.

ADD DETAILS

Look at your sentences. Think about these questions.

- What did you see? Tell about its colors. Tell about its size.
- What did you think or feel? Describe your feelings.
- What did you do? Did you do it *quickly*? Did you do it *slowly*? Write about *how* you did it.

Study the Model

Look at the model. What details did the writer add?

I had a problem with my puppy. Max was cute and cuddly, but he didn't know how to do much. My friend Jesse had a smart dog that could shake with his paw and fetch a stick. ~~do all kinds of tricks.~~ I wanted Max to do tricks too. I worked with Max every day after school. First, I taught him to shake. Then I taught him to fetch. Next, I even taught him to roll over! Finally, I showed Jesse all his tricks. I was so proud. Maybe I will be a dog trainer when I get older.

TECHNOLOGY TIP!

Use an online thesaurus. It can help you find interesting words that describe what happened and how you felt.

CHECKLIST: REVISING

☐ Is my story interesting to read?

☐ Are my ideas in order?

☐ Did I share interesting details?

☐ Do I have a good ending?

Practice

1. Reread your sentences. Use the Revising Checklist to make changes.
2. Give your draft to a partner.
3. Use the peer review worksheet on page 331 to give your partner feedback.

Name ______________________

Peer Review

Practice

Read your partner's draft. Then answer the questions.

Share your answers with your partner.

1. What I liked most was

____

____

2. One question I have for the author is

____

____

3. Here's one idea the author could use:

____

____

Edit

Writers reread their drafts to fix any mistakes.

They make sure that

- sentences and names begin with capital letters.
- sentences end with a period, question mark, or exclamation point.
- all words are spelled correctly.
- all sentences are complete.

PROOFREADING MARKS

- ¶ new paragraph
- ^ add
- take out
- ≡ Make a capital letter.
- / Make a small letter.
- (SP) Check the spelling.
- ⊙ Add a period.

Writers use these marks to correct errors on their drafts.

Study the Model

Look at this student model. What errors did the writer fix?

I had a problem with my puppy. Max was cute and cuddly, but he didn't know how to do much. My ~~frend~~ friend Jesse had a smart dog that could shake with his paw and fetch a stick. I wanted max to do tricks too. I worked with Max every day after school. First, I taught him to shake. Then I taught him to fetch. Next, I even taught him to roll over! Finally, I showed Jesse all his tricks. I was so proud. Maybe I will be a dog trainer when I get older.

Practice

1. Reread your draft. Fix any mistakes. Check for one type of mistake at a time.
2. Use proofreading marks to correct errors.

4

Publish and Present

Writers publish their writing to share it with others. They make a neat final copy. To publish, writers

- make sure there are no errors.
- write each word neatly.
- put space between each word and between each sentence.

TECHNOLOGY TIP!

Use technology to share your writing.

- Post your writing on a class Web site.
- E-mail it to your teacher or classmates.
- Show it on an electronic whiteboard.
- Make an audio recording. Save it as an audio file. Then others can listen to it on an mp3 player.

CHECKLIST: BEFORE YOU PUBLISH

- ☐ Did I tell a story about something that happened?
- ☐ Did I use interesting details?
- ☐ Did I put my ideas in order?
- ☐ Did I use temporal words?
- ☐ Did I tell how I felt in the ending?
- ☐ Did I fix all mistakes?

Practice

1. Give your draft one more look.
2. Write or type a neat final copy.
3. Add drawings or photos.
4. Share your writing with others.

Use this rubric to help you evaluate your writing.

Writing Rubric: Personal Narrative

	Goals	Yes	Need to Fix
Organization	I include a beginning, middle, and end.	☐	☐
Ideas	I tell about a real experience that happened to me. I use interesting details.	☐	☐
Voice	It sounds like me when I read it aloud.	☐	☐
Word Choice	I use describing words to tell about actions, thoughts, and feelings.	☐	☐
Sentence Fluency	I use temporal words to show what happened first, next, and last.	☐	☐
Conventions	I use correct spelling and punctuation.	☐	☐

4

Story

A story is made up by the writer. Stories are often told to entertain readers. What is your favorite story? Why?

Features of Stories

Good stories

- have **characters**.
- tell what the characters **do**.
- use **details** to describe characters and events.
- tell events in sequence, using **temporal words** such as *first*, *then*, and *finally*.
- have a **beginning, middle,** and **end**.

Story: Model

Look at the model. Find the answers to these questions.

1. Who is the main **character**?
2. What **temporal words** does the writer use?
3. What happens at the **end**?

The Smart Little Turtle

My name is Rocky. I am a little green turtle. My friends Priscilla and George are big white geese. We all live near Paddle Pond. One day, I noticed that the pond was drying up! We needed a new home. I told my friends to fly around and look for a new pond.

Right away Priscilla and George flew off. Soon they returned and said they had found a big, beautiful pond where we could live. Priscilla and George took turns flying above me. They guided me very slowly to the new pond. It was a terrific new home!

1. Who is the main **character**?

   The text says:

   > My name is Rocky. I am a little green turtle.

   Rocky the turtle is the main character.

2. What **temporal words** does the writer use?
   - One day
   - Right away
   - Soon

3. What happens at the **end**?

   They guided me very slowly to the new pond. It was a terrific new home!

Writing Process

Now you are ready to write your own story.
Follow the steps of the writing process.

- Prewrite
- Draft
- Revise
- Edit
- Publish and Present

Prewrite

Writers plan a story before they write. They decide:

- **Where** will the story happen? **When** will it happen?
- Who are the **characters**?
- What **problem** will they solve?
- What will happen in the **beginning**, **middle**, and **end**?

4

Study the Model

Look at this student model.

Characters: Juanita, her friends
Where it happens: Juanita's house

Beginning:
Juanita is going to have a party. She worries no one will come.

Middle:
She watches out the window.
She waits for people to come.
She worries.
Finally kids start to come.

End:
Juanita had a great time. She didn't need to worry.

TECHNOLOGY TIP!
Does your school or class have an online message board? A message board can help you choose an interesting topic. You can post your ideas. Classmates can reply to your post.

Turn to page 341 to plan your own story.

Name ______________________

Plan Your Writing

Practice

Plan your story's beginning, middle, and end.

1. Who are the characters? ______________________
2. Where does the story happen? ______________________
3. Use this chart. Plan what happens in the beginning, middle, and end.

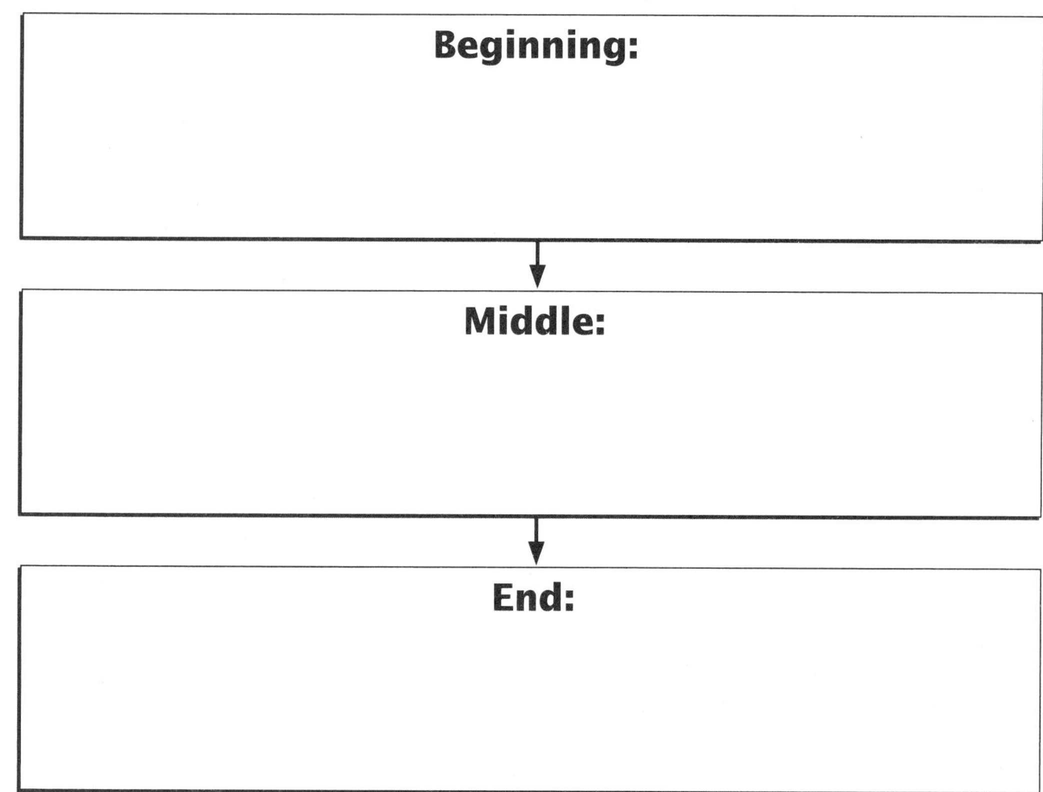

Draft

The next step is to write a first draft.

- A good **beginning** makes readers want to find out what happens next.
- Events are told in **sequence**, or order. **Temporal words** show what happened first, next, and last.
- Interesting **details** describe what happened and how characters think and feel.
- Finally, the **ending** tells how the problem was solved.

TEMPORAL WORDS

You can use these words in your writing:

first
next
then
later
after that
soon
last
finally

Study the Model

Look at the model. Find the details, temporal words, and the ending.

Juanita was worried. She was afraid that nobody would come to her party. She knew her friend Nikki would be there. What if no one else came? She would feel awful.

Juanita looked out the window. She didn't see anyone. After a while, she couldn't watch anymore. She went into the kitchen to wait.

Suddenly, the doorbell rang! She opened the door. There were kids on the porch. After a few minutes, more kids came.

Later, Juanita's mom asked her if she had fun. She said she had a great time! She had worried for nothing.

Here are the details that show how the character felt and thought.

- She was afraid that nobody would come to her party. She knew her friend Nikki would be there. What if no one else came? She would feel awful.

Here are the temporal words.

- After a while
- Suddenly
- After a few minutes
- Later

Here is the ending.

- Later, Juanita's mom asked her if she had fun. She said she had a great time! She had worried for nothing.

Practice

Use your ideas from the **Plan Your Writing** worksheet to write your first draft.

1. First, tell about the characters and their problem.
2. Then tell what happens in order. Use details and temporal words.
3. Last, write an ending. Tell how the problem was solved.

Revise

Revising makes writing clearer and more interesting. To revise, writers may

- add details to elaborate on the characters and events.
- delete words that don't tell about the topic.
- change boring words into more interesting words.
- move ideas around to make them clearer.

ADD DETAILS

Look at your story. Do you describe the action? Do you describe how the characters felt and thought? Here are some ways to add details.

- Tell about the way a character looks.
- Describe sounds the characters make or hear.
- Describe how characters do something. For example, do they move *quickly*? Do they talk *slowly*?

4

Study the Model

Look at the model. What details did the writer add? Which idea did the writer delete?

Juanita was worried. She was afraid that nobody would come to her party. She knew her friend Nikki would be there. ~~Nikki was her tallest friend.~~ What if no one else came? She would feel awful.

Juanita looked out the window. She didn't see anyone. After a while, she couldn't watch anymore. She went into the kitchen to wait.

Suddenly, the doorbell rang! She opened the door. There were kids on the porch. They grinned and shouted "Happy birthday!" After a few minutes, more kids came.

Later, Juanita's mom asked her if she had fun. She said she had a great time! She had worried for nothing.

TECHNOLOGY TIP!

E-mail your draft to your classmates. Ask them to share details you can add.

CHECKLIST: REVISING

☐ Is my story interesting to read?

☐ Are my ideas in order?

☐ Did I share interesting details?

☐ Do I have a good ending?

Practice

1. Reread your sentences. Use the Revising checklist to make changes.
2. Give your draft to a partner.
3. Use the peer review worksheet on page 348 to give your partner feedback.

4

Name ______________________________

Peer Review

Practice

Read your partner's draft. Then answer the questions.

Share your answers with your partner.

1. What I liked most was

____

____

2. One question I have for the author is

____

____

3. Here's one idea the author could use:

____

____

Edit

Writers reread their drafts to fix mistakes.

They make sure that

- sentences and names begin with capital letters.
- sentences end with a period, question mark, or exclamation point.
- all words are spelled correctly.
- all sentences are complete.

Writers use these marks to correct errors.

PROOFREADING MARKS

- ¶ new paragraph
- ^ add
- take out
- ≡ Make a capital letter.
- / Make a small letter.
- (sp) Check the spelling.
- ⊙ Add a period.

4

Study the Model

Look at this student model. What errors did the writer correct?

Juanita was worried. She was afraid that nobody would come to her party. She knew her friend Nikki would be there. What if no one else came? She would feel awful.

Juanita looked out the window. She didn't see anyone. After a while, she couldn't watch anymore. She went into the kitchen to wait.

Suddenly, the doorbell rang! She opened the door. There were kids on the porch. They grinned and shouted "Happy Birthday!" After a few minutes, more kids came.

Later, Juanita's mom asked her if she had fun. She said she had a great time! She had worried for nothing.

Practice

1. Reread your draft. Fix any mistakes. Check for one type of mistake at a time.
2. Use proofreading marks to correct mistakes.

Publish and Present

Writers publish their writing to share it with others. They make a neat final copy. To publish, writers

- make sure there are no errors.
- write each word neatly.
- put space between each word and between each sentence.

TECHNOLOGY TIP!

Use technology to share your writing.

- Post your writing on a class Web site.
- E-mail your writing to your teacher or classmates.
- Show your writing on an electronic whiteboard.
- Make an audio recording. Save it as an audio file. Then, others can listen to it on an mp3 player.

4

CHECKLIST: BEFORE YOU PUBLISH

☐ Did I have interesting characters?

☐ Did I use good details?

☐ Did I tell the events in order?

☐ Did I use temporal words?

☐ Did I write a good ending?

☐ Did I fix all mistakes?

Practice

1. Give your draft one more look.
2. Type or write a neat final copy.
3. Add drawings or photographs, if you wish.
4. Share your writing with others.

Use this rubric to evaluate your writing.

Writing Rubric: Story

	Goals	Yes	Need to Fix
Organization	I include a beginning, middle, and end. I tell events in order.	☐	☐
Ideas	My characters have a problem to solve. I use interesting details.	☐	☐
Voice	My story sounds natural when I read it aloud.	☐	☐
Word Choice	I use describing words to elaborate on the events.	☐	☐
Sentence Fluency	I use temporal words to show what happened first, next, and last.	☐	☐
Conventions	I use correct spelling and punctuation.	☐	☐

4

Standard 4–6

4

Lesson A

The Writing Process

You have an idea you want to write about. How do you turn that idea into a finished project? You can use the writing process. Many writers use these five steps. The writing process helps writers shape ideas into writing.

1. Prewrite
- Decide why you are writing and who will read it.
- Choose a topic.
- Gather ideas.
- Organize your ideas.

2. Draft
- Use your notes from prewriting.
- Get your ideas down on paper.
- Don't worry about mistakes.

3. Revise
- Add details and ideas.
- Delete ideas that are off topic.
- Substitute more interesting words.
- Rearrange sentences or parts of sentences.

4. Edit
- Check your spelling.
- Fix punctuation mistakes.
- Fix capitalization mistakes.
- Fix other grammar mistakes.

5. Publish
- Choose a format.
- Neatly print or type a final draft.
- Add visuals.

6. Present
- Share with your audience.

In this lesson you will find out more about the steps in the writing process.

- Prewrite
- Draft
- Revise
- Edit
- Publish and Present

Prewrite

First, writers make a plan.

- They think about a **topic**.
- They gather their **ideas**.
- They **organize** ideas.

4

Study the Model

Look at this student model:

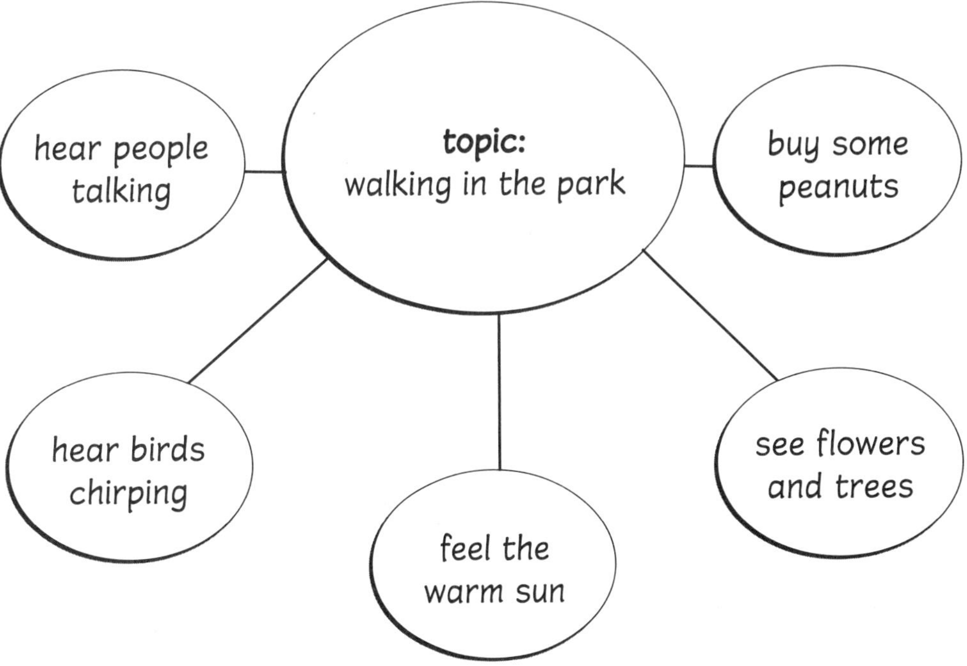

TECHNOLOGY TIP!

Does your class have a message board? Use it to post ideas. Classmates can reply. They can help you think of good ideas.

Practice

Make a plan for your writing. Follow these steps.

1. Choose a Topic

What do you want to write about? Think of some topics. Make a list of your ideas.

Share your topics with others. Which topic do they like best? Choose a topic to write about.

2. Gather Ideas

What will you say about your topic? Think of details to share. Ask others for ideas.

3. Organize Ideas

Many writers use an idea web. They organize their ideas in the web.

Turn to page 358 to practice on your own idea web.

Name ____________________

Idea Web

Practice

Write your topic in the middle. Write or draw details in the outer circles.

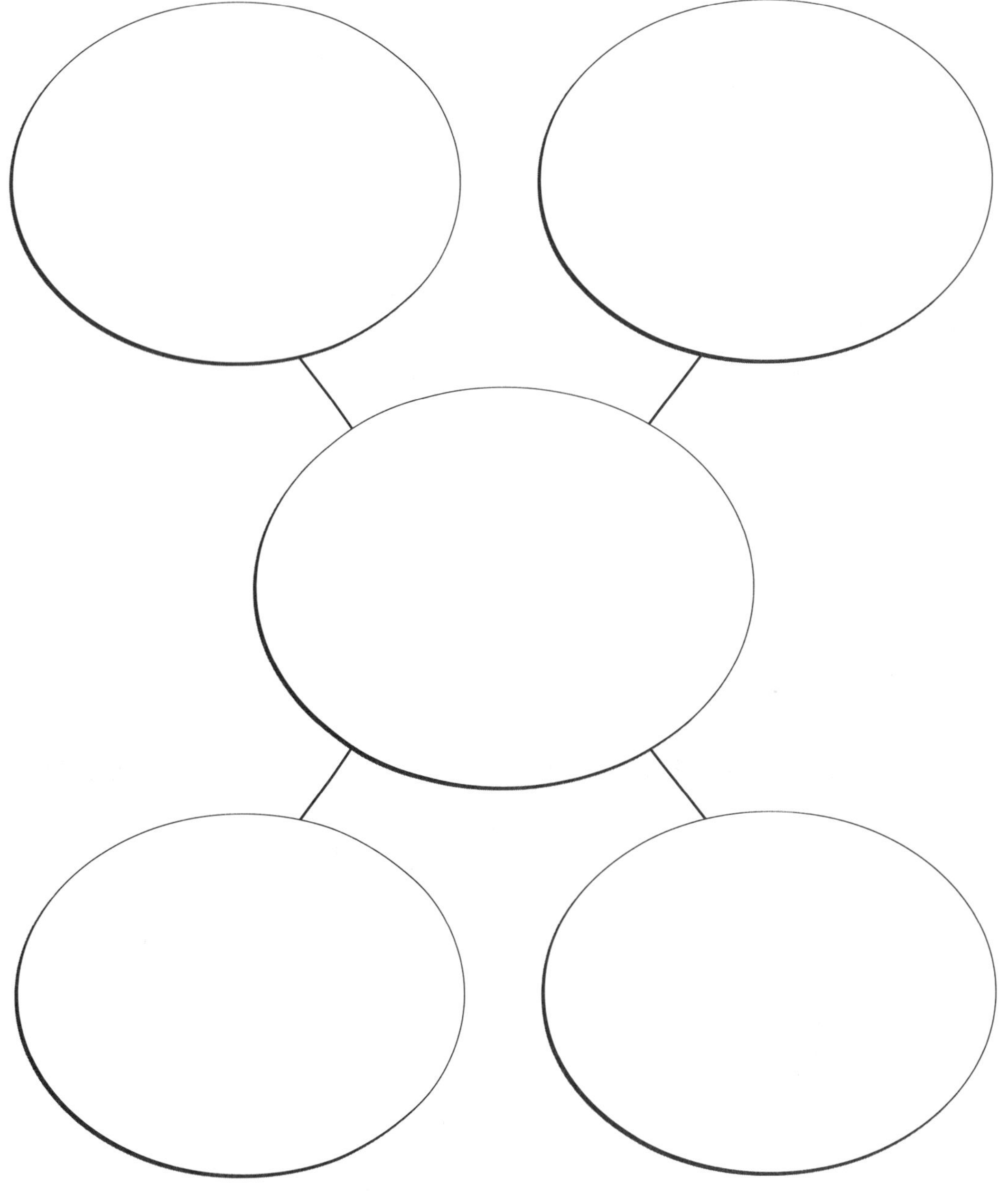

Draft

Next, writers put their ideas into sentences. They write as much as they can. They don't worry about making mistakes. They will fix them later when they revise.

Study the Model

Look at this model.

Mom and I took a walk in the park. We heard birds chirping. We heard people talking. We saw green leaves and flowers. We got some peanuts. They tasted fresh and salty. At the playground, I went down the slide. It was smooth and warm from the sun. I love to walk in the park.

TECHNOLOGY TIP!
Use a computer to type your draft.

4

Practice

Now write your own draft. Follow the directions.

1. Write a Beginning

Write a beginning. Share your topic. Make your beginning interesting. That way, readers will keep reading.

2. Write the Middle

Look at your idea web. Write sentences that tell about your topic. Use good details. Use only details that tell about your topic. Leave out details that tell about other things.

3. Write the Ending

Write an ending. Tell how you feel about your topic. Give readers something to think about.

Revise

Revising makes ideas clearer. It makes writing more interesting. To revise, writers may

- add details.
- delete ideas that don't tell about the topic.
- change boring words to more interesting words.
- move ideas around so they are clear.

4

Study the Model

Look at this model. What changes did the writer make?

Mom and I took a walk in the park.

We heard birds chirping. We heard people ~~talking~~ chatting. The air smelled fresh and clean. We saw green leaves and red flowers. We got some peanuts. They tasted fresh and salty. At the playground, I went down the slide. It was smooth and warm from the sun. I love to walk in the park.

TECHNOLOGY TIP!

Did you type your draft? You can e-mail it to a classmate or your teacher. They can type comments and send it back to you.

Practice

Now revise your own draft. Follow the directions.

1. Make Your Own Changes

Reread your sentences. Use this checklist to make changes.

Revising Checklist

- ☐ Is my topic clear?
- ☐ Are my ideas in an order that makes sense?
- ☐ Do I have enough details?
- ☐ Do all my details tell about my topic?

Peer Review

1. Give your draft to a partner.
2. Use the peer review worksheet on page 364 to give your partner feedback.

4

Name ______________________

Peer Review

Practice

Read your partner's draft. Then answer the questions.

Share your answers with your partner.

1. What I liked most was

____

____

2. One question I have for the author is

____

____

3. Here's one idea the author could use:

____

____

Edit

Writers reread their drafts to fix any mistakes.

They make sure that

- sentences and names begin with capital letters.
- sentences end with a period, question mark, or exclamation point.
- all words are spelled correctly.
- all sentences are complete.

Writers use these marks to correct errors on their drafts.

PROOFREADING MARKS

- ¶ new paragraph
- ^ add
- take out
- ≡ Make a capital letter.
- / Make a small letter.
- (sp) Check the spelling.
- ⊙ Add a period.

4

Study the Model

Look at this model. What errors did the writer fix?

Mom and i took a walk in the park. We heard birds chirping. We heard people chatting. The air smelled fresh and clean. We saw green leaves leafs and red flowers. We got some peanuts They tasted fresh and salty. At the playground, I went down the slide. It was smooth and warm from the sun. I love to walk in the park.

Technology Tip!

Fix spelling mistakes on the computer. Use the mouse. Put the cursor after the incorrect letter. Hit the Delete key. Type the correct letter.

Practice

Follow these directions to edit your draft:

1. Reread your draft. Fix any mistakes. Check for one type of mistake at a time.
2. Use proofreading marks to correct errors.

Publish and Present

Writers publish their writing to share it with others. They make a neat final copy. To publish, writers

- make sure there are no errors.
- write each word neatly.
- put space between each word and between each sentence.

TECHNOLOGY TIP!

Use technology to publish your writing.

- Type your draft on a word processor.
- Save your work often.
- Learn how to add clip art.

Share your final draft.

- E-mail it to your teacher and classmates.
- Post it on your school Web site.
- Show it on an electronic whiteboard.
- Make an audio recording. Save it as an audio file. Then others can listen to it on an mp3 player.

4

CHECKLIST: BEFORE YOU PUBLISH

- ☐ Did I stick to my topic?
- ☐ Did I share good details?
- ☐ Did I write an ending?
- ☐ Did I fix all mistakes?

Practice

1. Give your draft one more look.
2. Write or type a neat final copy.
3. Add drawings or photos.
4. Share your writing with others.

Lesson A

Use the Research Process

What do you want to learn about? You can do research to learn about it. Research helps you find answers and learn new things. After you research, you can write a report to share what you learned.

Work with a small group to research a topic. Follow these steps.

- Make a Plan
- Find Information
- Organize and Summarize Information
- Make a Presentation

4

Make a Plan

To begin researching, you need a plan.

What topic will you research? Where will you find information?

1. Choose a Topic

First, choose a topic. What do you want to learn about? Would you like to learn about animals? Would you like to learn about life cycles?

Look at this example:

> **Our topic is:** plants
> **We chose this topic because:**
> We want to learn how seeds become plants.

2. Ask a Question

Next, ask a question about the topic. Questions ask *who*, *what*, *when*, *where*, *why*, and *how*. You will do research to answer your question.

Look at this example:

> **Our question is:** How do seeds become plants?

The Make a Plan worksheet is on page 372. You will fill it in as you work with your small group.

4

Name ______________________

Make a Plan

Practice

Discuss topics with your small group. Think of questions you have. Choose a topic and ask a question. Write them in the blanks.

1. Our topic is

____

____

We chose this topic because

____

____

2. Our question is

____

____

Find Information

How will you answer your question? You will find information.

1. Gather Sources

It is a good idea to look at many sources. Each source can tell you different things about your topic. Here are some good sources:

- nonfiction books about your topic
- textbooks
- safe Web sites
- encyclopedias
- observations

Look at this group's ideas. What sources will they use?

Question: How do seeds become plants?

Sources we could use:
- Find books about plants and life cycles.
- Plant a seed and observe what happens.

4

2. Take Notes

Choose one of your sources. Write down the title. Write down the author's name. Look for facts about your topic. Write them in the Make a Plan worksheet.

Source 1:

- *Life Cycles of Plants* by Jordan Andrews

Notes:

- Seeds need soil, water, and light.
- The seed sprouts and becomes a plant.
- First, the root pokes through the seed. It grows in the soil.
- The part near the seed pokes through the soil. That's the stem.
- The leaves start to grow.

3. Make Observations

What can you learn about your topic by making observations? Record what you see. Add your notes to the Make a Plan worksheet.

Planting a Seed	
Day 1	Put seed in soil. Put it by the window. Watered it.
Day 4	Seed sprouted. The seed case is poking out of the soil. We can see the stem.
Day 5	The stem is standing up straight.
Day 6	First leaves appear.

The Find Information worksheet is on pages 376–378. You will fill it in as you work with your small group.

4

Name ______________________________

Find Information

Practice

Record your sources.

Write the author and the title.

If the source is a Web site, write the URL.

1. Gather Sources

> Example:
> *Life Cycles of Plants* by Jordan Andrews

1. ______________________________

2. ______________________________

3. ______________________________

Name ______________________

2. Take Notes

Now take notes about your topic.

Source 1

____
____
____
____
____

Source 2

____
____
____
____
____

Source 3

____
____
____
____
____

Name ______________________

3. Make Observations

Record any observations you make. Add notes and drawings.

____

____

____

____

____

Organize and Summarize Information

It is time to sum up your ideas and put them in order.

Sequence Ideas

Put your ideas in order. Use a chart like this one. What goes first? What goes next? What goes last?

4

These students found out how a plant grows.
They put their ideas in order.

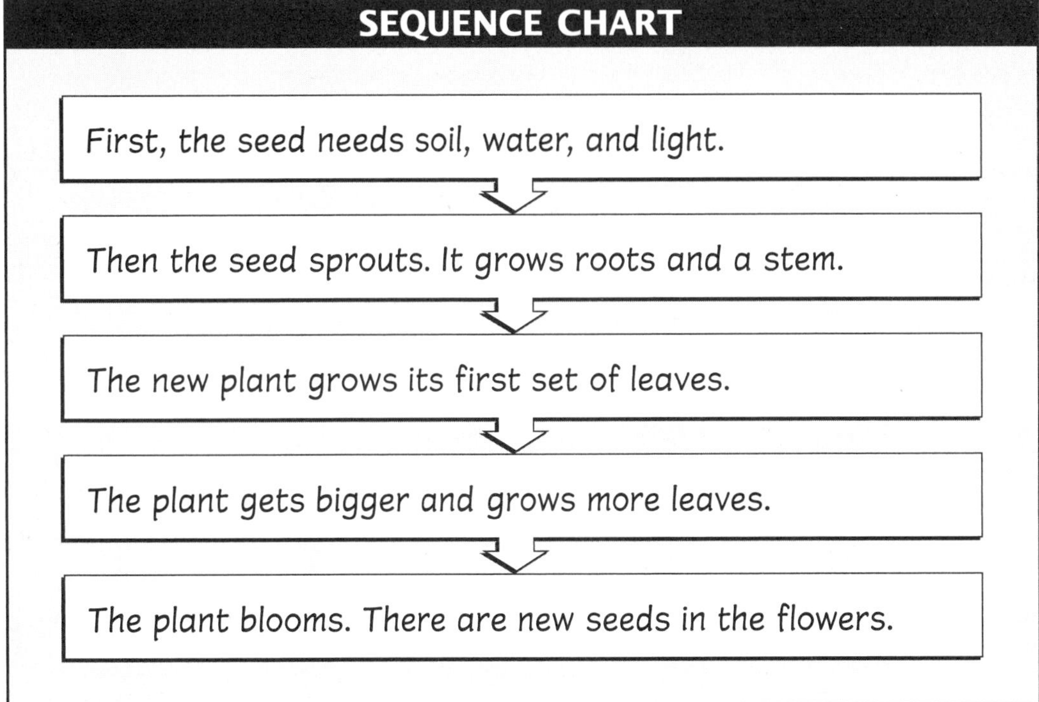

Practice

The Organize and Summarize worksheet is on page 381. Complete it with your small group.

Name ______________________________

Organize and Summarize

Practice

Look at your notes. Sum up the important ideas.

Put them in an order that makes sense.

Our research question is ____

____

____

Present Your Findings

You may wish to write a report to share what you learned from your research.

To write a report:

- Begin by telling your topic. Tell what question you asked.
- Then share the answer you found.
- Include important facts and details.
- Add drawings or photographs.

Here are some other ways to share your findings:

- Give a speech.
- Do a demonstration.
- Build a Web page.

What are some other ways you could share?

Practice

Share your findings. Share your research question and tell what you learned. Include facts, details, or examples.

To learn more about writing and presenting reports go to Writing 4.1 Lesson B **Write to Inform or Explain** on page 284.

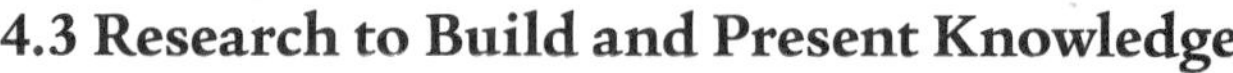

Lesson B

Answer Questions

How do you answer questions? There are many ways to answer questions. Finding answers is an important skill for researching and writing. In this lesson you will find out how to answer questions using these strategies.

- Use What You Know
- Find It in the Text
- Put It Together
- Use the Text and Your Head

Use What You Know

You can answer some questions on your own. Use what you already know.

Read this question.

Question: What is your favorite animal?

You don't need to look for an answer to this question in a book or other resource. You already know the answer! The answer is in your head. Use what you know to answer the question.

Find It

You need to look for the answers to some questions. There are many resources you can use. You can look in books. You can ask someone. You can read an article on a Web site.

> Animals live in many places. Birds live in nests. Rabbits live in holes. Foxes live in dens.
>
> Animals eat many things. Birds eat insects. Rabbits eat plants. Deer eat plants too. Foxes eat small animals, such as mice.
>
> Animals move in different ways. Birds fly. Rabbits hop. Deer and foxes walk and run.

Question: Where do rabbits live?

The answer to this question is underlined in the text.

Animals live in many places. Birds live in nests. <u>Rabbits live in holes</u>. Foxes live in dens.

Animals eat many things. Birds eat insects. Rabbits eat plants. Deer eat plants too. Foxes eat small animals, such as mice.

Animals move in different ways. Birds fly. Rabbits hop. Deer and foxes walk and run.

4

Put It Together

Sometimes you need to look in more than one place to find an answer to a question. It is like a puzzle. You need to search for the pieces and put the pieces together. Then you can answer the question.

Question: What are rabbits like?

Where is the answer to this question? It is found throughout the text. You need to search for it in many places. It is underlined in the text below.

> Animals live in many places. Birds live in nests. <u>Rabbits live in holes</u>. Foxes live in dens.
>
> Animals eat many things. Birds eat insects. <u>Rabbits eat plants</u>. Deer eat plants too. Foxes eat small animals, such as mice.
>
> Animals move in different ways. Birds fly. <u>Rabbits hop</u>. Deer and foxes walk and run.

Use the Text and Your Head

You can use what you already know to answer some questions. You can use the text to answer other questions. Sometimes, you need to use both your head and the text to answer a question.

Question: Why can birds live in trees?

Where is the answer to this question? The text doesn't tell you the whole answer. It does give you a clue, however. Use the text clue and your head to figure out the answer. The clue is underlined below.

> Animals live in many places. Birds live in nests. Rabbits live in holes. Foxes live in dens.
>
> Animals eat many things. Birds eat insects. Rabbits eat plants. Deer eat plants too. Foxes eat small animals, such as mice.
>
> Animals move in different ways. Birds fly. Rabbits hop. Deer and foxes walk and run.

The answer is:
Birds can fly up to the tree branches.

Turn to pages 388–389 to practice answering questions.

4

Name ____________________________

Answer Questions

Practice

Read the passage. Then answer the questions. Tell where you found the answer.

Whales are warm-blooded mammals. They need to come up to breathe the air above the water.

Whales live in the water. They need water to hold their weight. Oceans and seas are the homes for whales. Many whales live in the Antarctic Ocean.

Many whales travel in groups. They make low sounds to talk to each other. They make high sounds to find food and to travel. They eat baby shrimp and plankton.

1. How do whales breathe?

____

Where did you find the answer? Circle one.

In my head	In the text
Searched the text	In my head and the text

2. What is your favorite ocean animal?

___

Where did you find the answer? Circle one.

In my head In the text

Searched the text In my head and the text

3. What are three things that whales do?

___

Where did you find the answer? Circle one.

In my head In the text

Searched the text In my head and the text

4

4. Why do you think whales travel in groups?

___

Where did you find the answer? Circle one.

In my head In the text

Searched the text In my head and the text